The Clinical Use of the Revised
Bender-Gestalt Test

The Clinical Use of the Revised

Bender-Gestalt Test

by

Max L. Hutt

Psychology Department
University of Michigan
Ann Arbor, Michigan

Gerald J. Briskin

Psychological Consultation
Service
Detroit, Michigan

GRUNE & STRATTON   **NEW YORK • LONDON**

Library of Congress Catalog Card No. 60-13430
Printed and bound in the United States of America

Contents

Table of Plates

Preface

The primary purpose in writing this book was to make available in one volume the rationale and methods of projective interpretation of the Revised Bender-Gestalt Test. Ever since the introduction of this method of interpretation by the senior author in 1944, there has been a growing interest and utilization of this type of approach. Unfortunately, no comprehensive discussion of the rationale or methodology was then available, although a number of articles, case studies and special seminars were presented over the years. Each clinician utilizing the kind of approach which the senior author advocated was compelled, therefore, to employ the scattered bits of data and examples of methodology that were available, and each, in turn, "projectively" interpreted the suggestions for interpretation or tried to follow or to modify consciously the leads that had been offered. However, it soon became apparent that some workers were making different assumptions about methods of interpretation than had been proposed and that some of the differing results which were reported were based, in part, on these varying assumptions.

Only the tests of time and further clinical and research efforts will finally lead to the most fruitful methods of utilizing this and similar clinical techniques. The present work is itself evidence of the changes which have been developed since the method was first utilized. Just as important as methodology, and even more important at the present state of our knowledge, is an explicit statement of the theoretical structure on which this technique rests. For it is by the development of theory that fundamental advances in knowledge can be most effectively made. Tests and modifications (or even rejection) of the theory can lead to significant increments to our knowledge far more than endless, empirical and haphazard research efforts. It is hoped that the present work will contribute, therefore, to this testing of theory as well as to enriched clinical productivity.

But a theory of projective testing depends, also, on a theory of diagnosis, and the fields of clinical psychology and psychiatry have, as yet, had little to say about such a theory. This is not surprising since our knowledge of psychopathology is still admittedly insecure. Since the introduction of Kraepelin's system of classification at the turn of the century, diagnostic methods have been based essentially on his conception of assessment. Sporadic efforts have been made to modify this approach, notably by a few psycho-analysts, but clinical practice has not been able to move very far from the rudimentary conceptions of classification. Indeed, this volume reflects this state of affairs to a considerable extent. Nevertheless, a newer conception of diagnosis, that of psychodiagnosis, resting on dynamic rather than be-havioral assumptions and leading to different kinds of predictions about individual behavior is urgently needed, for reasons which this volume at-tempts to make clear. Hence, a second purpose in writing this work has been to make communicable our efforts toward the development of a more modern conception of a theory of diagnosis.

As an explicit method of diagnosis, some branches of American science have given short shrift to the inferential approach. American psychology has held high the banner of empiricism, seeming to reject all other phenomena as being "unscientific." It is noteworthy that physics, on the other hand, has been able to utilize other methods than empirical ones—and with considerable benefit. Neglect of inferential methods, especially in clinical diagnosis, is likely to result in neglect of highly important kinds of behavioral phenomena and to reduce the possibilities of certain kinds of important predictions con-cerning behavior. This conclusion is probably even more pertinent to source phenomena than to surface phenomena—and sources of behavior are under constant scrutiny in clinical work. A corrective emphasis is badly needed, the present writers believe, if we are to make bold progress in clinical psy-chology. Hence, we have attempted to spell out and to illustrate (and even to document the effectiveness of) an approach to inferential diagnosis, using perceptual-motoric behavioral phenomena as the subject matter of discussion. We trust that this effort will find a sympathetic reception, not only in clinical psychology but in psychology more generally.

It is difficult to acknowledge appropriately all of the people who have con-tributed to this volume, directly and indirectly. In addition to those indi-viduals who are specifically cited in the text and in the references, we wish to acknowledge the assistance of the many clinicians who by their constructive inquiries and suggestion have stimulated many innovations in our thinking and clinical work. Nameless, too, must remain the many clinical students who have participated in clinical seminars and have suggested new ideas. And, of course, the clinical patients who have come for help, and by their coming have contributed of themselves toward the furtherance not only of their own welfare but the welfare of science, rightfully deserve special grati-tude. Finally, the devoted and friendly assistance of Mrs. Gloria Briskin and of Miss Wilma Schmadtke in carrying forward the secretarial and typing chores is acknowledged with thanks.

PART I

I

The Revised Bender-Gestalt Test and

Its Clinical Application

The *Revised Bender Visual-Motor Gestalt Test*, referred to hence-forth more simply as RBGT, had its origin in the work of Bender,[4] who was interested in exploring the theoretical and clinical implications of visual and motor responses in normal and psychopathologic conditions in children and adults. Some of the clinical uses of the test in this form are discussed in her monograph.[4] The importance of this technique was fully documented in that work and led one of the present authors to explore the possibilities of using the test materials in terms of their implications for projective behavior.[22] We shall discuss the history of the development of these two divergent but supplementary approaches in Chapter II, but we wish to present, first, some of the more important clinical possibilities of the projective approach.

It is held as axiomatic that all behavior is a resultant of both conscious and unconscious drives. In some kinds of behavior, conscious factors play the decisive, in fact, almost the all-inclusive, role. Such kinds of behavior may be relatively simple or relatively complex but have as a distinguishing feature the phenomenon of deliberate choice or conscious determination. We assume, all too commonly, that as civilized human beings we make such deliberate choices in most of our behavior, but clinical and experimental evidence suggests that even the most simple types of behavior may, more frequently than we suspect, be influenced by unconscious factors. Not only slips of the tongue, forgetting, and distortions of reality (such as prejudice entails), but even style of speaking, choice of words, postural adjustments, and facial expression reveal the extent to which unconscious factors are interlaced with acts in which awareness and conscious intent seem, at first, to play the decisive role.

It is problematic how decisive unconscious factors are in a great many

3

aspects of our everyday behavior. The role of such factors becomes clearer when we examine dream material or when we analyze neurotic behavior. In fact, it is widely accepted that psychopathologic phenomena are largely determined by unconscious drives which find expression in symptomatic acts and in characterologic traits. The overt phenomena are resultants of the interplay of many factors but, it is clear that unconscious factors are crucial to their occurrence. In more nearly normal behavior the influence of unconscious forces is more difficult to assess, but clinical studies of normal individuals under conditions of stress highlights the finding that even normal behavior consists, in part, of large components of derivatives from the unconscious.

From a clinical viewpoint, an evaluation of the nature and functioning of unconscious phenomena is essential both for a determination of the nature of the psychopathology, if present, and for the management and alleviation of psychopathologic behavior. Through such evaluation, an understanding of the dynamics of behavior becomes attainable and appropriate consideration can then be given to problems of prediction and management. There are now available a wide variety of methods for assessing unconscious and underlying aspects of behavior, with the vast majority of such methods depending upon some form of verbal communication. To note a few, we can mention structured and unstructured interviews, free association techniques, objective personality measures, verbal projective techniques, dream material, and role playing situations.[13, 26, 28]

With many patients, verbal techniques of clinical diagnosis may produce sufficient evidence concerning the nature and role of unconscious factors, particularly in the hands of a sophisticated clinician. But then there are others for whom such diagnostic approaches hardly suffice. Let us examine some of these types of individuals for whom other evaluative measures are needed and consider the nature of the problems which they present. We shall then be in a better position to consider the clinical values of the RBGT, the main purpose of this chapter.

First of all, let us consider those patients who are unable or unwilling to produce a sufficient sample of verbal behavior for appropriate clinical analysis. Such persons may be grouped into a number of broad categories. *Category I* consists of patients whose speech functions are markedly inhibited. We would place in this category patients showing extreme withdrawal behavior, such as catatonia or marked schizoid involution, those with intense degrees of anxiety having a markedly impairing function on speech and writing, those revealing severe depression, and phobic patients for whom verbal communication may have elements of severe threat. In cases of this general kind, the sample of verbal behavior which can be elicited may be insufficient for evaluative purposes. More than this, the sample which is obtained may not be representative of the core conflicts or may be so meagre that only indecisive formulations can be attempted either with respect to the precise nature of the psychopathology or with respect to its severity. Consider, for example, a person under acute and intense anxiety. Unless we have supplementary evidence concerning the origin of the anxiety, we may infer, incorrectly, that the inhibited and meagre sample of verbal behavior which is communicated reflects a severe and persistent anxiety reaction, although in fact the individual is reacting only to an acute and stressful situation in real life. Thus, without corroborating evidence, we may underevaluate the level and strength of ego resources and we may be unable to identify the presence or absence of conflicts which are germane to his functioning. Cases of the type we have called Category I confront us, then, with two related clinical problems: *the problem of the representativeness of the sample of behavior which has been elicited,* and *the problem of difficulty in identification of the underlying psychopathology due to an insufficient sample of behavior.*

Category II consists of those patients suffering from some form of intracranial pathology. Here, the problem is clearly different from that of patients in Category I. In the first place, samples of verbal behavior are usually inadequate to determine either the presence of brain damage or the nature of such damage, if present. Except for some specific types of brain pathology, and not always even then, verbal behavior does not reflect directly the presence or kind of damage which may be present. In the second place, it may not be possible to diagnose early or mild forms of brain damage on the basis of the usual neurologic procedures. On the other hand, disturbances in perception or in some aspects of motor behavior, or in the combined visual-motor response may, and often do, reveal evidence concerning underlying pathology.[33] More than this, since the way in which a person reacts to intracranial pathology is a function of his personality, there is need of a technique which reflects both aspects of the problem. Except in extreme cases, verbal behavior fails to provide the needed information.

Category III consists of that group of patients who are able to respond fully but whose verbal behavior does not reveal the precise nature of their psychopathology. It includes those whose verbal defenses have held up much better than other aspects of their defenses, and those who deliberately distort their verbal communication in order to create a false impression. The first type includes, for example, patients who defend against a psychotic disorganization by compensatory, obsessive defenses involving speech or writing. Every experienced clinician has met such individuals who, in diagnostic consultation or in psychotherapy, appear to represent problems in obsessive neurotic reactions and whose underlying psychotic features (usually schizophrenic process phenomena) do not appear until a later stage of disorganization has become frankly apparent. As a consequence, differential diagnosis by means of samples of verbal behavior alone can be quite faulty. The second type includes the malingerer and similar kinds of problems. Here, skillful attempts to distort and mislead the clinician may succeed by virtue of ample samples of verbal behavior that convey the impression desired by the malingerer and inadequate samples of other, relevant aspects of the behavior. Since, most commonly, malingering occurs among individuals who are, in fact, maladjusted, the problem of differential diagnosis may become exceedingly complex. It is much more difficult to simulate faulty visual-motor behavior since the patterns of culturally acknowledged psychopathology in this area are not as readily accessible to the malingerer as are the verbal patterns of gross psychopathology. In later chapters we discuss particular ways in which malingering may be detected with the RBGT and the underlying pathology, if present, evaluated.

The last group, *Category IV*, contains a miscellaneous population of patients. Here we would group the illiterates, the uneducated, and the foreign-born—all of the individuals who are handicapped in verbal communication. Such persons are likely to give atypical test protocols on instruments designed for individuals with normal linguistic skills who have had "normal" cultural-educational opportunities for language development. Tests like the RBGT, on the other hand, relying primarily on relatively simple, relatively culture-free visual and motor performance, do not place such individuals at an undue disadvantage. To the extent that perceptual-motoric performance reflects basic aspects of the personality, as we believe it does, such tests have uncommon advantages for this group. We might add that these advantages highlight the potential, in general, for eliciting aspects of behavior and personality by means of perceptual tasks.

An analysis of the types of individuals for whom nonverbal techniques of personality assessment are especially desirable more clearly reveals possibilities for the use of such tests as part of the total battery of diagnostic procedures which the clinician may employ. Let us start with the last category. Since perceptual-motor tests are relatively little influenced by the specific educational and cultural characteristics of the environment, the skills that are involved have not been transmitted as part of formal educational and learning experiences. Rather, they constitute the incidental ways of adaptation which the individual has developed.[26] Probably, for this reason, such tests may reveal more of the underlying, the veneer-free characteristics of the personality, relatively unencumbered by the formal features of the culture. In this respect, it may be well to remember that linguistic communication conceals as well as reveals as we learn to adopt the defensive measures which the culture provides. Examples of this phenomenon may be found in such obscurantist defenses as *rationalization* and *intellectualization*. Perceptual-motor tasks do not offer such a handy screen and may therefore be useful not only for individuals in *Category IV* but for many other clinical patients.

Related to this aspect of the more internal, less external features of perceptual-motor tasks is the nature of perceptual behavior itself and of motoric behavior itself. The basic and pervasive aspects of such skills are learned during the first few years of life.[26] It is conceivable that many aspects of the style of perception, for example the adient and integrative aspects of perception, are strongly influenced by the total affective nature of the infant's earliest experiences.[26] Similarly, the motoric styles of behavior are strongly influenced by emotional experiences of the "socialization years"—the anal period. Consequently, perceptual-motoric behavior, especially in its projective aspect during the elaboration phase of the RBGT, offers important leads to early sources of conflict in the personality and to source traits and primary features of the personality.*

Another advantage of tests like the RBGT is that they offer a sample of projective behavior when such samples are not readily apparent in the verbal behavior. Not only is this useful for patients falling in Category I but it often provides supplementary information even when verbal behavior is not associated with unusual problems in the personality. Thus, the RBGT is useful as a supplement to the tests and procedures relying primarily upon verbal communication; it is especially useful when the samples of verbal behavior represent inhibited functions or are not representative of the personality; and it is useful when verbal behavior, although ample, nevertheless tends to conceal some important aspects of the personality.

The RBGT has been found especially useful for patients with organic difficulties. As noted above, perceptual and motoric difficulties appear in the behavior of such patients long before their verbal behavior is affected. Moreover, since there is no one-to-one relationship between organic deficit and personality characteristic, the RBGT is helpful in that resultants of the organic damage together with other manifestations of the personality may be secured in the same record. As we shall see later, in Chapters IV and XII special procedures may be utilized to highlight both the organic and non-organic features of the response.

These and other considerations lead to a variety of clinical uses to which the RBGT may be put. For the sake of simplicity, we may list them as follows, noting that these functions tend to overlap and that the listing is mainly for purposes of summary and emphasis.

1. The RBGT is useful as a *buffer test* (or "warm-up" test) as part of the psychodiagnostic battery, since it is usually not highly threatening and is enjoyed by most patients.

---

*See Chapters V and VI for discussion of this issue.

2. The RBGT is useful as a *supplementary technique* in rounding out the personality assessment so that verbal behavior is not overemphasized in the total evaluation of the patient.

3. The RBGT is useful when tests involving *minimal examiner-patient interactions* are required. Some patients are unduly and adversely affected by such interactions.

4. The RBGT is useful for *illiterates,* the *uneducated,* and *culture-deprived* patients for whom samples of behavior based on verbal skills provide a biased or invalid evaluation.

5. The RBGT is useful in the *differential diagnosis of mental retardation,* especially in cases in which cognitive inhibition due to emotional factors conceals intellectual potential.

6. The RBGT is useful for patients whose *verbal behavior tends to conceal some aspects of their emotional difficulties,* such as patients with strong intellectualizing and rationalizing defenses.

7. The RBGT is especially useful in cases in which *malingering* is suspected.

8. The RBGT is useful in the *differential diagnosis of intracranial pathology.*

9. The RBGT is useful in differential diagnosis in cases in which *neurotic defenses may conceal an underlying psychotic process.*

10. The RBGT is useful in delineating specific aspects of the dynamic features of the personality, such as *latent homosexuality, difficulty in interpersonal relations,* and *problems in identification.*

11. The RBGT is useful in uncovering *problems of fixation at the oral and anal periods.*

12. The RBGT is useful in assessing *degree and kind of improvement* (or decrement) *following various therapeutic measures.*

13. The RBGT is useful in *research studies* relating perceptual-motoric behavior to personality dimensions.

II

History: Development of the Revised Bender Visual-Motor Gestalt Test

As its name implies, the Bender-Gestalt test is historically rooted in classical Gestalt theory. The nine geometric figures that comprise this test were taken from a larger sample of visual patterns developed by Wertheimer and utilized by him for the study of Gestalt principles involved in perception.[46] The results of these and other studies have become widely known as various laws of perception: namely, the laws of pregnanz, closure, nearness, and the like. These findings follow from a fundamental assumption of Gestalt psychology: that there is a biologically innate tendency on the part of living organisms to organize perceptual experiences in terms of unified configurations. Other studies by the Gestaltists suggest that there is a temporal factor in perception so that configurations are perceived in a state of changing into "good form." Biological factors determine these perceptual abilities and they develop to their fullest only when the organism has reached the critical point of maturation.

Mature, healthy perception, according to the Gestalt school, consists of the integration of a triad of factors: (1) the innate tendency of organisms to organize perceptual data as it is affected by (2) temporal factors and (3) maturational level. It tends to follow that any other factors, emotional, toxic, organic or traumatic, that affect these perceptual processes would also be reflected in some way in the patient's response (verbal or written) to his perceptual experience. However, no attempt was made by Wertheimer or his contemporaries to explore these clinical implications of perception. Their concern was essentially that of determining laws of normal perceptual experience.

During the late 1920's, Lauretta Bender, who was profoundly influenced by the Gestalt school of psychology, adapted Wertheimer's figures for clinical use. Working on the assumption that the primary unit of psycho-

9

logical data is the organized configuration or Gestalt, she began to investigate the manner in which these Gestalten were experienced in various clinical syndromes. Her approach has as its rationale the basic position that in certain pathologic conditions a change has taken place in the maturational development of the perceptual processes which leads to the tendency to perceive forms in a more primitive manner. Depending upon the nature of the specific condition, these changes may be due to an arrest of development, to degenerative or traumatic changes in the brain, or to the autistic regression that takes place in schizophrenia. From her clinical studies, Bender concluded that *Wertheimer's* patterns, which she renamed "A Visual-Motor Gestalt Test," were useful in diagnosing disorders in which changes in Gestalt perception occur. The specific clinical entities to which Bender feels this test is applicable are mental deficiency, schizophrenia, aphasia, organic brain damage, certain toxic disorders, and manic depressive psychosis. In manic depressive psychosis, Bender is of the opinion that no changes take place in Gestalt perception but that the "energy of association" that characterizes this disorder is such as to cause elaborational doodling upon the basic Gestalt form which in itself is diagnostic.[4]

Bender further asserts[4] that one does not expect to find disturbances of perception or of visual Gestalt function in the psychoneuroses. Furthermore, she subsequently expressed doubt that the Bender-Gestalt can be used projectively. Instead, she reaffirmed her position that this test is useful only in determining whether or not visual-motor disturbances have taken place, and if so, in relating them to the causative process, as she conceives this.

Nevertheless, in this same work she states that certain Gestalt forms could take on symbolic representation of an individual's unsatisfied infantile drives. When this statement is considered in relation to Bender's description of the use of the test in the manic depressive psychosis, it appears evident that she tacitly assumes that this visual-motor task measures something more than disturbances of Gestalt perception. This "something more" can be considered to be the unique behavior each individual brings into the testing situation which, through projection, may become apparent in the test protocol. That is to say, when a person is presented with these nine geometric figures in a relatively ambiguous situation and asked to make copies of them, he must proceed in a manner unique to his own past experience. His reactions reflect his "style of life" and he will structure or deal with the task at hand in some way that approximates his tendencies to be himself. In the test situation John Smith will tend to react the way John Smith characteristically reacts, and from these reactions the examiner can infer something of John Smith's personality characteristics.

Insight into the potential role of motor movement in revealing personality characteristics was provided by Mira.[28, 29] His studies in myokinesis led to the subsequent development of the Mira Myokinetic Test in which analysis of patients' repetitive reproductions of simple geometric forms is used diagnostically. Mira offered evidence that such factors as a patient's tendency, in drawing, to rotate a horizontally oriented progression of figures toward himself suggested aggression turned inward, whereas rotating the figures away from him suggested aggression directed toward others. He also studied variations in drawing that were made by the patient's dominant hand and contrasted them with distortions made by the nondominant hand, hypothesizing that the dominant hand revealed overt personality characteristics while the nondominant hand predicted potential behavior.

Though the Mira Myokinetic Test differs considerably from the Bender-Gestalt in terms of stimuli, demands on the patient and methods of work, they share in common a basic reliance upon visual perception and motoric behavior to allow the patient to project into the test situation.

Despite the potential of the Bender-Gestalt test for eliciting projective material, until the second World War, work with this test was primarily limited to its "traditional" use in elucidating the various kinds of responses which are characteristic of the clinical groups mentioned above. Analysis of the test was in terms of fundamental Gestalt principles, and there was virtually no concern with the mechanism of projection as it operated in the test setting.

During the Second World War, the increasing frequency of traumatic neuroses, neurotic and psychotic breakdown, and cases of organic brain damage gave urgent impetus to the need for simple tests which would enable the clinician to distinguish among various categories of clinical psychopathology and to ascertain whether there was any psychological evidence of injury to the brain. A complicating factor was the diversity of the clinical sample, since the recruitment of soldiers sampled widely differing levels of intelligence and types of educational background and cultural influence. Hence, it was necessary to find psychological instruments that would be useful in cases involving serious deficiencies in language or cultural deprivation. As a result of these and related considerations, Max Hutt devoted his attention to the problem of developing means for relatively rapid, nonverbal methods of personality evaluation. His previous experience with the Bender-Gestalt test had impressed him with the possible projective significance of the responses to this test, with the personality attributes associated with various styles of organizing the total pattern of response, and with the diagnostic value of the comments made by the patient during and after his performance. In his role as instructor at the Adjutant General's School for Clinical Psychology and later as Chief of the Clinical Psychology Branch of the U.S. Army, Hutt suggested modifications in the administration and interpretation of the Bender Visual-Motor Gestalt Test on the basis of considerable clinical experience with this test. He proposed the use of the test as a projective instrument and began to evaluate it in terms of the basic theory of projection. As clinical data accumulated, various test factors could be isolated and defined and served as initial bases for tentative interpretation of the findings obtained with this test. Subsequently, on the basis of further clinical experience and research, he published his tentative manual,[22] and with the assistance of F. L. Wells, he developed a set of modified Wertheimer figures. It was on these grounds that he called the new procedures the Revised Bender-Gestalt Test and introduced it as a projective instrument for use in military settings.

Approximately three hundred clinical psychologists received brief training in the clinical use of the Bender-Gestalt Test in the Army. They, in turn, gave impetus to the use of this test by indoctrinating their military and civilian colleagues in its use. The impact of these advances in the clinical use of the Bender-Gestalt is most clearly seen in the test's bibliography. Prior to World War II, excluding Bender's studies, there are virtually no references in the literature to the Bender-Gestalt test. Subsequent to the war, the Bender-Gestalt bibliography grew at a reasonably impressive rate, and the test is now generally afforded space in compendia dealing with clinical instruments.

In addition to the widespread clinical use of the Bender-Gestalt following the war, considerable research has been carried on utilizing this test. In general, this research has followed two basic trends: first, to clarify problems of scoring and develop objective scoring methods, and, second, to determine distinctive "patterns" of test behavior for various diagnostic entities. Implicit in this second approach is the attempt to test the specific validities of the Bender-Gestalt Test.

In 1948, Billingslea, who was introduced to the possibilities of the Bender-Gestalt test while in the clinical psychology program in the Army, published a monograph[5] which dealt with an objective scoring method and some validation data for the Bender-Gestalt. On the basis of Bender's and Hutt's suggestions regarding test determinants, he developed *his own* definitions of these determinants, restructuring them in two classes, *factors* and *indices*. Billingslea used the term *factor* to refer to clearly detectable test behavior which was observable in one or more of the Gestalt figures. On the other hand, *indices* involved a rather specific set of measurements of one figure, such as line length, angles, and the like. Thirty-eight factors were identified by Billingslea, and he utilized 137 indices to measure them. This was an unwieldy scoring system for which, according to Billingslea, some 15 hours were required to score a single record. He recognized the practical limitations of this scoring for clinical use, but proceeded to use this system to test the hypothesis that certain of his test factors would differentiate psychoneurotics from normals. It should be noted that Billingslea's study, like Bender's, made no attempt to

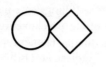

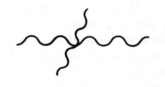

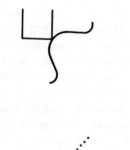

PLATE 1   The Revised Bender-Gestalt Figures.

test projective hypotheses. From this research, Billingslea concluded that, in general, the Bender-Gestalt could not differentiate psychoneurotics from normals, that specifically "Hutt's syndrome" for the psychoneurotic record could not be supported, and that the test factors and indices *he* (Billingslea) utilized tended to be unreliable and to lack validity.

Although Billingslea's selection of psychoneurotics appears to have been rigorous, his selection of normals was based on questionable criteria. But an even more fundamental question regarding this study is the manner in which he used his factors as diagnostic signs. The basic assumption of his scoring system is that certain test factors are pathognomonic indicators of neurosis. It is this misinterpretation of Hutt's original paper on the Bender-Gestalt test that apparently led Billingslea to conclude that his study could not support Hutt's syndrome. Hutt actually said, in discussing clinical syndromes, "It is important to understand the underlying psychodynamics revealed in the Bender-Gestalt drawings" (ref. 22, p. 12). Furthermore, the lack of validity that Billingslea found in factors from several of the Gestalt figures is to be understood in terms of this important point. The degree of distortion expected in the various figures will vary in terms of the specific symbolic value each figure has for each individual taking the test. For example, an individual manifesting specific castration anxiety might be expected to show shape distortion (Billingslea's factor) on figures 7 and 8, without significantly distorting any of the other figures.[5] Consequently, the interfigure validity of such a factor (shape distortion) would be low even though the clinical significance of such a factor might be quite high.

One final comment on Billingslea's scoring method may be noted. By attempting to get factor score for each Gestalt figure, he approaches the interpretive task in an atomistic manner, violating a fundamental Gestalt principle: the whole is greater than the sum of its parts. There is a characteristic of organization, interrelation between the figures, and general appearance of RBGT records, important for interpretation, that cannot be readily quantified, or perhaps cannot be quantified at all. This position reflects a controversy that still rages in contemporary psychology: whether or not clinical prediction is superior to actuarial prediction.

In 1950, Pascal, who had previously been a member of the military clinical psychology program, published in collaboration with Suttell, a book on this test.[33] In it, they present a relatively simple, objective scoring procedure and demonstrate its effectiveness in discriminating among normals, psychoneurotics and psychotics. Their scoring method utilizes a unitary score obtained from the *sum total* of the distortion in all the Gestalt figures. They do not feel that the test score is a pathognomonic indicator of specific clinical syndromes, but rather that the frequency of disturbances of Gestalt function would appear in the test record in proportion to the severity of the disorder.

The tabulation of these distortions would then serve as an index to the intensity of underlying pathology. On this basis, Pascal and Suttell suggest that certain critical scores can serve to classify test behavior into the gross categories of normal, neurotic and psychotic. Their reported research bears out this assertion. The important distinction between their scoring system and that of Billingslea is that their score is based on the summation of factors in the test as a whole, in contrast to Billingslea's partial scores. Nevertheless, both of these scoring systems only attempt to discriminate gross distinctions among classes of psychopathology. For a test to assume full usefulness as a clinical instrument, it must be capable of a variety of specific predictive discriminations and thus be able to supply the answers to questions such as: "What is the specific pattern of this neurosis?" or "What are this patient's areas of conflict?" or "What are this patient's characteristic defenses?"

Still another attempt to standardize and validate a scoring system for the Bender-Gestalt was reported by Gobetz in 1953.[11] He developed a set of some 82 scoring categories, presumably based partially on the previous work of Pascal and Suttell, Hutt, and Billingslea but defined essentially in his own manner. The intent of his investigation was to determine whether neurotics and normals could be distinguished from each other on the basis of these scoring categories. Gobetz concluded that: "The Bender-Gestalt Test, *as scored in the present study* (italics ours), is recommended as a screening device to be used as a supplement to other diagnostic tests rather than as an instrument for the elaborate interpretation of individual personality dynamics." He also was unable to replicate either Hutt's clinical findings or Pascal and Suttell's results with reference to neurotics.

However, a major shortcoming of the Gobetz study is that he failed to offer any data in his monograph on the reliability of the scoring of the test records investigated. He does not even indicate whether anyone other than himself was involved in this scoring. This is a crucial question since many of his scoring categories require *subjective* judgments.

Some of the comments above regarding Billingslea's study are also pertinent here, particularly as they concern the issue of pathognomonic indicators. In conclusion, it would seem that Gobetz has established the unreliability of his scoring categories rather than the unreliability of the Bender-Gestalt as an instrument for interpreting personality.

Hutt's contribution in the case of Gregor[23] indicated that the Bender-Gestalt test could function in this manner. Participating in a symposium on projective techniques, Hutt made a "blind" analysis of a Bender-Gestalt protocol and demonstrated the test's validity as a personality instrument. He was able to predict correctly such factors, among others, as the patient's current status, basic character structure, defensive hierarchy, sexual adjustment, psychiatric diagnosis and prognosis.

Though this symposium could not qualify as "research," it has significance in its implications for the potential of the Bender-Gestalt test. This is particularly true in terms of demonstrating how clinical material in a test can be interpreted to furnish highly specific predictions over a wide range of personality characteristics. By and large, Hutt's analysis points up the shortcomings of purely quantitative clinical techniques. Quantification is the *beginning* of one type of phase of interpretation. Other types of interpretation depend upon rigorous inferences deduced from the qualitative and quantitative interactions of various test factors. (See Chapters V and VI.)

Hutt has presented two other detailed and "blind" analyses of RBGT records in which the predictions derived from this test could be checked against criteria based on long-term clinical diagnostic studies and on the therapists' evaluations of the patient's progress.[25, 27] In each case, highly meaningful and precise predictions received striking corroboration. As Cronbach acknowledges, in his recent review of one of these studies, "Such test interpretation is often severely criticized as unscientific. In defense of the method, we may note that Hutt is able to give a *detailed rationale for each of his inferences* (italics ours). A much stronger defense is that his description of the patient agrees with the clinical picture given both from the MMPI self-report and in the therapist's notes. *Word for word,* we find confirmation there of *ineffectual defense through obsession, hostile impulses the subject fears to express, and so on*" (italics ours) (ref. 8, p. 581).

Research studies dealing with the projective potential of the Bender-Gestalt have been appearing in the literature since 1950. In 1952, Suczek and Klopfer[38] investigated the symbolic value of the Wertheimer figures that comprise the Bender-Gestalt Test. These figures were presented to a group of college students for their associations. The assumption was that people tend to perceive these designs in characteristic ways. Suczek and Klopfer's findings led them to advance tentative hypotheses regarding the symbolic value of each test figure.

Hammer[17] made specific tests of Suczek and Klopfer's hypotheses which dealt with the psychosexual values of certain B-G designs, attempting to isolate indices of phallic sensitization, castration feelings and reactions to castration feelings. The experimental group was composed of men who were to undergo sterilization under the eugenic laws of the State of Virginia. Men who were to undergo surgery other than sterilization were utilized as a control group. The testing was carried out on the day of surgery. Hammer found support for Suczek and Klopfer's hypotheses in his data. He was also able to isolate test factors that were significant in distinguishing the experimental group from the control group. The majority of these factors involved distortions of the elongated or phallic elements of the B-G figures.

In 1959, Byrd[6] published a study on the clinical validity of the B-G test which overcame some of the shortcomings of earlier research. Utilizing 15 of the determinants which were considered by Hutt to be signs of psychopathology, Byrd undertook to ascertain whether or not they could discriminate between "well-adjusted" children and children who had been diagnosed as being in need of psychotherapy. *The definition and scoring of the determinants studied followed Hutt.* The experimental and control groups were composed of two hundred children each, ranging in age from 8 to 15 years. The population was further divided into four subgroups according to age, each group consisting of 50 well-adjusted children and 50 children in need of therapy. One striking dissimilarity between the B-G administration utilized by Byrd and that advocated by Hutt was that in this study the subjects' drawings were limited to one side of a piece of $8\frac{1}{2}$ x 11 inch paper. Byrd's results "support the validity that the majority of test factors selected from Hutt are signs of personality adjustment." Furthermore, these factors operated in the direction predicted by Hutt. But Byrd acknowledges that his study was essentially a "sign" approach which demonstrated that certain test factors could grossly discriminate between adjustment and maladjustment. In sharp distinction to Billingslea and Gobetz, he goes on to conclude that: "Evaluation of a record involves far more than a listing of signs. The total test performance must be considered. . . . Finally, psychodynamic interpretations of the test signs presented by Hutt and others must still be considered hypotheses to be tested. . . ."

In a more recent study, Clawson utilized the B-G as an index of emotional disturbance in children.[7] In many respects, her experimental design is similar to that of Byrd, although she was also interested in evaluating some specific types of affective responses on the basis of B-G characteristics. The performance of an experimental group of disturbed children on the Bender-Gestalt was compared with the performance of a control group of "normal" children. The B-G was scored using determinants suggested by Hutt.

Clawson found that the following determinants were significant, in the direction predicted by Hutt, at a significant level:

1. Use of white space. Figures widely spread over the page indicate aggressive, rebellious tendencies, whereas figures compressed into a small area suggest withdrawal.

2. Changes in the size of the figures. Decreased size of the drawings was found to be related to withdrawal behavior, overcontrol and inadequate channels of expression. Uneven size of figures was related to low frustration tolerance, irritability and acting out.

3. Closure difficulty. This factor was associated with difficulty in establishing and maintaining effective interpersonal relationships.

4. Sequence. Orderly sequence was typical of well-adjusted children, while, rigid and confused sequences were characteristic of the maladjusted children.

Changes in curvature tended to be present in the B-G records of the experimental group in the predicted directions, but the absolute occurrence of this determinant was not sufficiently frequent so that it could be tested statistically.

These studies are significant in that they offer experimental evidence that B-G determinants can discriminate between emotional disturbance and types of emotional adjustment. This type of discrimination, however, is essentially the prediction of surface traits, and the research evidence described above does not necessarily support the authors' contention that one of the primary values of the RBGT is its usefulness in enabling the clinician to identify and describe process phenomena. Some experimental evidence on the latter problem is now available in a recent study by Story.[37]

In a well-controlled study using alcoholics as the experimental group, Story derived several hypotheses from personality theory and theory of psychopathology concerning expected dynamics common to the alcoholic syndrome. He then selected RBGT determinants which had been suggested by Hutt as being related to these dynamics.

An example of the manner in which Story developed these hypotheses warrants reproduction here:

"A low tolerance for frustration and corresponding avoidance of stress are among the most frequently observed behavior patterns in alcoholics. Characteristically, this behavior is to be seen in withdrawal or escape from the demands of interpersonal activities rooted in a deep-seated and pervasive anxiety about interpersonal relations in general. Briefly, rather than endure the frustrations of unsatisfactory cathexes, the alcoholic chooses to flee from them. We hypothesize that this psychological blocking in the face of interpersonal demands should be evident in the response behavior to certain designs having intersecting, overlapping, or joined lines, e.g., designs A, four, six, and seven. On the revised design six, for example, where the stimulus may be perceived as either two intersecting sinusoidal lines or two separate, nonintersecting, yet still touching sinusoidal lines, we hypothesize that alcoholics will perceive and reproduce these lines in the latter fashion, i.e., as nonintersecting, significantly more often than the control subjects."

In a similar manner, the following hypotheses were formulated:

1. In their elaboration of design seven, alcoholics will tend to reproduce them as nonoverlapping hexagons.

2. In elaborating design two, alcoholics will either change the columns of circles to the vertical plane, use solid straight lines, or reverse the direction in slant of the circles.

3. Alcoholics will count the dots on design five, aloud or with a finger or pencil.

4. Alcoholics rotate the upright hexagon in design seven more than five but less than 20 degrees to the left.

Story's findings support each of these hypotheses at significant levels of statistical significance. An additional unpredicted finding was that the alcoholic experimental group tended to *elaborate* figure 6 (the sinusoidal curves) as waves, ripples, rivers, torrents, lakes, etc., significantly more (p. <.005) than the control group, a rather provocative finding in the case of alcoholics.

Another major area of research, along more classical lines, has been concerned with this test's effectiveness in differentiating patients with organic brain damage from patients without such damage.

One test factor receiving research attention has been rotation. Fabian[10] found that children with reading difficulty tended to rotate horizontally oriented designs to a vertical orientation. He suggested that this "verticalization persistence" reflected infantile patterns of behavior. Hanvik and Anderson[19] found that patients with focal brain lesions rotated B-G figures significantly more often than control patients. In a later study, Hanvik[20] determined that 80 per cent of an experimental group of children who made one or more rotations on the B-G also had abnormal EEG tracings.

On the other hand, other studies present contrasting findings in terms of the B-G's effectiveness in diagnosing brain damage. On the basis of B-G records, Sullivan and Welsh[39] were unable to differentiate between a group of children with poliomyelitis and a normal group. However, the organic lesions in the experimental group may have been below the medulla and consequently might not have been expected to reflect in B-G performance.

In testing recall or memory reproduction of B-G figures, Hanvik and Anderson[19] found no significant difference in recall in the test records of an organic and normal group. However, they presented no data regarding their criteria of how similar the recalled figure had to be to the original stimulus to qualify as an acceptable reproduction.

In dealing with this problem of memory reproduction of B-G figures, Reznikoff and Olin[34] measured differences in *good recall* scores of organic and schizophrenic patients. They found that schizophrenics reproduced significantly more figures from memory than organics. But when a form of weighted recall score which took into account distortions in the recalled figure was utilized, the difference between these groups was not significant.

In a later study, Olin and Reznikoff[32] tested recall in groups of normals, schizophrenics and organics. The recall criterion in this study was scorability of the recalled design by the Pascal and Suttell scoring method. Highly significant differences in recall were found distinguishing normals from both organics and schizophrenics, but differences between organics and schizophrenics were insignificant.

Goldberg[12] also studied the diagnosis of organic brain damage from the B-G test. Three groups of judges, psychology staff, psychology trainees, and nonpsychologists at a Veteran's Administration hospital were asked to differentiate organics from nonorganics on the basis of the patients' B-G performances. The combined diagnostic accuracy of all groups of judges was 68 per cent correct selection, a finding that was significantly better than chance. Surprisingly, the nonpsychologists did as well as the professional judges. In a subsequent exploration, Goldberg asked "one of the country's foremost authorities on the Bender test" to analyze the test protocols. This expert correctly identified 25 out of 30 records (83 per cent accuracy). Goldberg concluded that ". . . real experts in the technique may perform with increased diagnostic accuracy on this task, [and] it is conceivable that they might be able to communicate whatever interpretive refinements they possess."

The·studies cited above, despite their varied and often contradictory findings, suggest that the Bender-Gestalt does have potential as a diagnostic instrument for the evaluation of organic brain damage. Positive findings in well-controlled studies cannot be casually dismissed. Where contradictory results occur, analysis often indicates that the experimental criteria in similar studies may have varied considerably. In other instances, the researcher often concludes that the B-G is unreliable when a more parsimonious explanation is that his particular analysis or "system" may be unreliable.

Certainly, replication of contradictory studies is both desirable and necessary. But when such replication is done, the original study should be repeated as it was originally performed and only then should new controls, modified criteria, and the like be added for additional analysis. It is the authors' contention that the questions raised regarding the Bender-Gestalt, or, for that matter, any other technique in psychology, can be resolved only on the basis of a careful research approach. This also places an additional burden upon research workers: that they fully define all their procedures operationally when they publish their research.

When these studies and demonstrations are taken together, they begin to mass research and clinical evidence to support the role of motoric-perceptual tasks such as the RBGT in the diagnosis of organic brain damage as well as the projective analysis of personality. But more specifically, these studies offer validity to the contention that the RBGT can be used to predict both surface traits and process phenomenon. It has been only relatively recently that the "research validity" for the RBGT has begun to catch up with the "clinical validity" that competent clinicians have offered for this test. At this point, only time will give us sufficient perspective to assess fully, with relevant research and clinical evidence, the strengths and weaknesses of the RBGT as a projective instrument.

The following four chapters are concerned with presenting a rationale for the administration and projective use of the RBGT. We shall draw upon pertinent research and clinical evidence, wherever possible, to support our interpretive proposals.

III

General Problems in Psychodiagnosis

In order to use a diagnostic tool properly the interpreter must possess a number of basic attributes. It goes without saying that he must fully understand the tool which he is employing: its underlying rationale; its methods of standardization; its techniques of administration; its clinical and experimental findings; and its values and limitations in assessing the particular phenomena which it is designed to assess. However, having all of these attributes for a particular test or for a series of diagnostic techniques does not qualify the interpreter as a clinician. Without much more he is merely a psychometrist, although he may be a very good one and he may contribute significantly along this line. We should not underestimate the functions and values of the psychometrician, but, by the same token, we should not confuse them with the functions and values of the clinician.

The distinction between the psychometrician and the clinician is important for both theoretical and practical reasons. The former, according to our definition, has developed the appropriate knowledge and skills to use and interpret one or more instruments or techniques. He is not necessarily well versed in general psychology, much less in psychopathology or even the psychology of personality. He has not been trained to relate psychometric findings to other aspects of the clinical history or to other clinical data and to management and therapeutic measures for the patient. He has knowledge and respect for the research findings concerning reliability and validity of the measures he employs, but he is not in a professionally appropriate position to go beyond these confines of his knowledge. And, as we shall see, clinical diagnosis, or, as we prefer to term it, *psychodiagnosis*, characteristically involves much more. Psychodiagnosis includes the gathering and weighting of *all* relevant evidence concerning the patient, an analysis of the causative factors in the present condition, a description of the present condition in terms of the total syndrome which is evident, an evaluation of the dynamic characteristics of the present condition (under what conditions does "what" give rise to "what"), and prediction of those changes that may be expected from present and/or altered circumstances.[26]

As we have indicated, the distinction between these two types of clinical workers is important for theoretical reasons. We are still in the stage of development concerning psychopathology in which we make the assumption that a given psychiatric syndrome constitutes a unique entity, separate and distinct from all other such entities. Some workers have begun to question this assumption and others have already rejected it. However, as long as the assumption is maintained, it is necessary to postulate that a given configuration of *behavioral characteristics* defines a particular clinical entity, with its own etiology, development, and final outcome. Thus, psychiatry arrived at the basic classification of "mental disorders" on the discovery that certain kinds of behaviors tended to belong to one set of etiologic conditions while others belonged to other conditions. This type of descriptive psychiatry had to assume a one-to-one relationship between behavioral configuration and underlying psychopathology. Almost all types of objective tests of personality make the same assumption: that there is a one-to-one relationship between measures of behavioral traits and psychiatric abnormality. Yet, clinical and research evidence has accumulated which challenges this fundamental assumption.

For one thing, it has been demonstrated that some patients who fall within one psychiatric category may later belong in other categories. For example, a group of patients originally diagnosed as manic depressive were later found, in a follow-up study, to be more appropriately classified as manic depressive in some cases, as schizophrenic in others, and in still different categories in others, on the basis of the later development of their condition and their changing behavioral characteristics.[21] Increasing doubt has been cast on the essential homogeneity of schizophrenia as a distinct disease entity. Certainly, patients with simple and hebephrenic forms of this condition differ from others with paranoid and catatonic forms in certain important respects: amount of regression, susceptibility to treatment, spontaneous remission, and the like. Similarly, many individuals who show, as a result of severe and acute trauma, reaction patterns which closely resemble essential psychoneurotic conditions differ significantly from the usual varieties of psychoneurotics. Clinical evidence gathered during the years of the Second World War amply substantiated this.[15] Finally, persons with neurotic character disorders are difficult to distinguish, on the basis of behavior syndromes alone, from other persons with classical neurotic disorders of the same type.[26] All of these and related observations suggest that there is no one-to-one relationship between current psychiatric grouping and underlying psychopathology. Parenthetically, this is probably one of the important reasons psychiatric criteria of psychopathology are relatively low in reliability.

If, then, there is no complete relationship between symptoms or behaviors

and type of psychopathology, it follows that there cannot be a simple, uni-
lateral relationship between a test sign or test measure and a psychiatric
condition. On the contrary, the meaning of a test sign or a test measure may
acquire different meanings depending upon the *constellation of which it is a
part* and depending upon the *conditions which give rise to it*. The former
may be tested statistically by evaluating the differential power of various configurations of signs. Indeed, this is the pattern which has been followed by
a considerable portion of contemporary clinical research. Although this
development has offered some promise, notably in some problem areas such
as the differential diagnosis of brain pathology, the results have not been
altogether encouraging. This should not have been unexpected since configurations of behavioral measures can only, if done adequately, contribute
to the accuracy of predicting configurations of behavior; i.e., psychiatric
categories, and we have seen that psychiatric categories may be of limited
value. The second qualification noted above, the condition which gives rise
to the behavior, may, and on theoretical grounds should, give better results.
For here we can begin to deal with *process phenomena* which have a certain
independence of the resultant behavioral phenomena. Before we proceed to
elaborate this point, let us hasten to add that we are not recommending
abandonment of the use of configurational measures, for they do have
important uses. Rather, we are emphasizing the value of process phenomena
in differential diagnosis and the theoretical basis for their use.

By *process phenomena* we mean derivatives as directly related as possible
to the underlying causative factors. We can make the meaning of this definition clearer by comparing the usual behavior phenomena with process
phenomena. An individual, for example, displays the behavioral trait of
passivity. His passivity may be readily recognized as such, and techniques
may be employed for measuring the intensity of this trait. But the behavioral
trait in one person may mean something far different from what it may
mean in another. In one case, it may be the direct expression of avoidance
or withdrawal defenses. In another, it may signify the presence of some
degree of conflict over dependency needs. In still another, it may represent
a compromise reaction or a reaction formation to latent aggressive strivings.
The accurate assessment of the trait, then, tells us little or nothing concerning
the underying processes which have given rise to the behavior. The trait may
be conceived of as the indirect resultant of varying underlying process
phenomena. Passivity may, thus, occur as the end-product of various conflict-
ing drives and their "resolution" in terms of the ego's resources in dealing
with them in the context of a given cultural setting.

The same argument may be made concerning all such traits—which are
more accurately described as *surface traits*.[26] Traits are usually conceived

of as more or less persistent behavioral tendencies. Most present-day objective tests of personality measure such surface traits, and evidence concerning them has considerable value in predicting the likely, overt, behavioral phenomena which an individual may manifest. However, to deal adequately with the person who has these traits, or even to understand him, we need to know something of the conditions which give rise to them. And to do this we have to understand, measure, and deal with the primary process phenomena which produce them.

Process phenomena, then, refer to the dynamics of the behavioral resultant. They are rooted in the latent tendencies which each individual possesses— in the drives which motivate his behavior. Rarely do drives manifest themselves directly in observable behavior, not even in the most primitive of people. It may be said that the more civilized an individual is, the more indirect is the expression of primary drives. Civilization imposes the requirement that drives be socialized: inhibited, delayed, and integrated in socially appropriate ways. Psychopathology, for different reasons, defensive in character, also requires that only the most indirect expression of drives be permitted. But in both types of instances, the overt behavior can only offer obtuse clues to the processes which give rise to them. It might be added that it is easier to infer the drives which motivate behavior in the case of a "normal," civilized individual than in the case of a psychopathologic individual; their expression in behavior is more direct in the former instance.

Projective tests, and clinicians employing projective hypotheses, probe for the underlying processes which give rise to a given form of behavior. When a person is asked to respond to a relatively unstructured stimulus, we assume that in the process of organizing his response to this situation, he will display some derivatives of the underlying drives, that he will project these drives into the "test" situation. If we obtain a number of samples of such projective behavior, we are then able to infer the presence and intensity of such drives. Note that we said *infer*, for projective behavior is still overt behavior and merely gives us greater access to underlying phenomena, not direct measures of them. There are two conditions, then, for effective use of projective behavior: a sufficient sample of such behavior under varying conditions, and an inference concerning the sample in respect to the kind of process which gave rise to it.

Now we are in a position to begin to understand the role of the clinician. He will wish to employ, like the psychometrician, those techniques and measures which will enable him to assess, with an appropriate degree of reliability and validity, the presence and intensity of the important traits which the patient manifests. But he will go one step further; he will try to relate these findings and the findings of the case history to the intrapsychic conditions which give rise to them. In this latter step he will employ, among other things, devices like projective tests in order to assess process phenomena. To do this he will need more than good instruments for eliciting projective behavior. He will need to know how to go about making certain kinds of inferences from the results of such "tests," and, if he is scientifically trained, he will carefully weigh the significance of the evidence, look for corroborating and contrasting findings, and integrate all of this data into the most parsimonious explanation he can offer for the problems which have been raised.

To play the role of the clinician appropriately, and not just to *play at* the role of clinician, the individual will have acquired certain kinds of training and be able to use this training effectively. In the first place, he will have secured training in general psychology so that he has sophistication about the findings relative to behavior in general. Among other things he will know: something about the principles of scientific method; basic information concerning biological mechanisms; what has been learned concerning behavioral development, including sensory processes and perception, and patterning of behavior; the values and limitations of current theories of personality; the present state of our knowledge concerning psychopathology; and theories and techniques relating to therapeutic process. Of these, perhaps of greatest importance for the clinician is his knowledge of personality theory and psychopathology, for without these he cannot make appropriate inferences about his observations and test findings, nor can he check his initial hypotheses about a patient against other plausible, perhaps more plausible, hypotheses. With these assets in his training, he can, if he is not too rigidly bound in his *initial* speculations about a patient, begin to think through the possible implications of his data.

The last point probably needs some elaboration if its meaning is to be clearly conveyed to the reader. There are probably two great limitations in the work of a clinician which may interfere with his effectiveness considerably. One of these is an insensitivity to relevant data. This may come from inadequate knowledge about behavior, and especially about psychopathologic behavior, or it may come from an inability to use himself appropriately as an observer. Both of these may be improved by training, although there may be serious limitations to what training can accomplish with some types of personality. The other limitation, also related to both training and personality, concerns the "freedom to speculate wisely" about a patient. The data, once they have been gathered, must be examined in such a variety of ways as to maximize the significance which they may have. The clinician must be able to entertain relevant hypotheses about the patient, even when the evidence is at first quite tentative, check these hypotheses against all relevant findings, and reject or confirm the hypotheses on the basis of the evidence. Scientific training too often overemphasizes the checking of hypotheses and under-emphasizes the ability to develop creative and frankly speculative hypotheses. Both types of creative thinking are essential in developing and checking hypotheses about a patient.

Projective tests offer access to data related to underlying process phenom-ena, and these data may then be manipulated in various way to germinate and corroborate inferences concerning psychopathologic behavior. They are less useful in defining specific psychiatric syndromes which have been derived from an examination of clusters of overt behavior. The latter task may well be left to good history and case analysis procedures or to more exactly defined, objective tests of personality. Critics of projective tests who have pointed out that validation studies of such tests have not had great success are essentially correct. The criticism is valid but it overlooks another, at least equally important point. The designation of a particular psychopath-ologic syndrome tells us very little about the meaning of a particular patient's behavior.

And here, again, we must emphasize our contention that a psychiatric label has little personal significance for dealing with the patient. It defines the broad category of people who have the designated, overt behavioral features, but it does not warrant the assumption that *all* the people with that label have the same conflicts, the same drives, or even necessarily the same psycho-pathology. To acquire knowledge about these matters requires more appro-priate assessment of the nature of the drives, the nature of the conflicts, the nature of the ego resources, and the other specific characteristics of the psychopathology. This is the clinician's task: describing or measuring the character structure of the individual, not merely designating the behavioral syndrome which is present. And this is the task with which the therapist must deal if he is to have meaningful data to manage effectively his interpersonal relationship with the patient. One might highlight this argument by stating that a psychiatric label offers leads to the general category of patients to which the individual belongs and is most useful for administrative reasons, while a psychodiagnostic evaluation of the patient offers leads to the specific features of the dynamic processes which a particular patient possesses and to the appropriate management of this patient.

The RBGT is particularly useful in gaining access to underlying process phenomena. It can be used, as some studies have done, to derive scores based on clusters of perceptual errors, to define psychiatric categories or severity of psychopathology.[4,11,33] As we have indicated, such uses have limited value, and there may be other and more efficient ways of securing such results. Or the RBGT may be used to get at underlying process phenomena which give rise to the resultant behavior. Because the ways in which an individual perceives, organizes, and executes responses to a task of this kind maximizes the projective aspects of his behavior, this test offers leads to projective hypotheses about the patient.

We shall now offer some leads to this aspect of psychodiagnosis and then present a sample of a projective analysis of a test protocol to concretize the discussion. Chapter II and Chapters V and VI, especially, offer more detail concerning this method.

When a person is asked to examine a simple Gestalt design, he may or may not perceive it accurately. Whether he does or not depends, in the first instance, upon the biological maturation of the organism. Without such maturation the organism is unable to perceive mature Gestalten.[46] If, in a particular instance, the individual is able to perceive some of the more mature Gestalt forms (more mature as determined on the basis of normative data) but is unable to perceive accurately some of the less mature Gestalten, we have prima facie evidence that some personality disturbance, and not inadequacy in general maturation, is responsible.

Now, assuming that discrepancies of the kind suggested above do appear, what can be inferred? There are several patterns of perceptual distortion, each of which is related to different kinds of defenses. If, for some idiosyncratic reason, the Gestalt is perceived as threatening to the individual, it may be defended against by *over-adient* or *over-abient* behavior. Abient behavior represents an attempt to withdraw from the perceptual stimulus. In extreme instances, the individual may "black out" the stimulus (or part of it) and not "see" it at all. Some cases of hysterical blindness manifest this kind of defense. Or he may see the stimulus as smaller than it is in reality. Some cases of micropsia represent this kind of defense. Or he may perceive some parts of the stimulus as relatively smaller than other parts. Some cases of withdrawal and repressive responses to curved portions of stimuli represent this kind of defense against the symbolic meaning of curved lines to some patients. On the other hand, he may show an over-adient response, probably a more mature and active type of defense, by increasing the perceptual size of the stimulus or of part of it. In such instances, the patient is able to deal more directly with the stimulus than when he "withdraws" by decreasing size, but he also makes some compensatory efforts in dealing with it.

In addition to gross distortion in size, another type of general defense pattern may be employed. The patient may show the type of distortion which we have called *retrogression*. In such instances, the patient substitutes a more primitive Gestalt for a more mature Gestalt, such as the substitution of a circular form for a diamond, or a substitution of loops for dots, or of nonoverlapping characteristics for overlapping characteristics.

Still another type of distortion is represented by perceptual rotation in which the figure is perceived as if its axis has been rotated to some degree. There are various hypotheses related to different degree of rotation, and to direction of rotation, but, in general, rotation appears to represent feelings of impotency in reacting to the stimulus and to the psychological characteristics which it represents.

These three examples of perceptual distortion may suffice at this point to indicate the projective possibilities of ascertaining relatively pure examples of defensive behavior. As we shall see, there are many other types and subtypes of perceptual distortion, many of which have been studied experimentally and clinically.[4, 6, 7]

But the RBGT involves not only perception but also motoric behavior. Here, we can utilize examples of aberrant motor behavior as leads to underlying needs, defenses, and conflicts. For example, a very simple indication of anxiety is the inability to make a smooth, even, motor movement, resulting in incoordination and impulsive motor behavior. Another example is the tendency to exaggerate or to decrease movements in either the horizontal or vertical planes, tendencies which are related to conflict in dealing with authority figures and close interpersonal relations, respectively.[28, 29] Still another is the difficulty in executing relatively simple motor responses involving the crossing of lines or the closing of figures, difficulties related to fear of or inability to maintain emotional cathexes with other people.[7, 37] Each of these behaviors may, of course, be the result of disturbances in the perceptual as well as motoric sphere.

Finally, the RBGT involves the planning, organizing, and revising of plans in the successive phases of the *basic* method: the *copy* phase, the *elaboration* phase, and the *association* phase. The arrangement on the page (or pages) of successive drawings, the use of space, the use of margins, the ability or inability to modify or to correct discrepancies—these and many other features involving planning and organizing of successive responses—give us projective evidence of characteristic personality styles employed by different patients. For example, the crowding of many drawings into a small corner of one page, or the need to separate each drawing from every other drawing, or the inability to shift the placement of the figure in accordance with the reality features of the drawing and the space available represent different kinds of needs and defenses that may be present in different psychiatric syndromes; yet these syndromes have basic underlying features common to all or to some. We shall defer to Chapters V and VI a more detailed consideration of such features, but point out here that there are correlates in underlying personality features of such styles of organizing behavior responses.[23, 28]

As an introduction to the use of the RBGT as a projective clinical instrument, the following case illustration is presented.* The rationale and the sources of the specific hypotheses which are discussed are presented in some detail in Chapters V and VI.

We are told that Tom, one of a pair of identical twins, is heterosexual and is 27 years of age. We have no information, unfortunately, on his methods of work during the Bender test.

Taking a general overview of Tom's Bender reproductions, we note that he has arranged the figures on two successive pages in correct sequence, and further that he has spontaneously numbered each of the figures from 1 to 9. The figures are considerably enlarged in size and this enlargement *tends to* increase with each successive drawing. (Note, for example, that Tom has drawn five of the figures on the first page, and has drawn four figures on the second page, using the entire page in each case.) Although he has utilized space liberally, the spacing of successive figures is appropriate to the size of the reproductions. With this initial information, we are able to offer some hypotheses based on Tom's general approach to this problem. These are: he tends to be outgoing, labile and assertive in his approach to a new and relatively unstructured situation, showing no essential evidence of overt anxiety in his test behavior (although we can infer that the increase in size is compensatory for some degree of latent anxiety); he tends to order his world, using external controls (the numbering) to gain some degree of mastery or self-assurance (a subhypothesis is that he uses the service of compulsive defenses to achieve this end-product); the appropriate, but liberal, use of white space suggests that his assertive drives are at least reasonably well socialized.

A second set of general observations may be made, taking note of the relatively heavy line drawings he utilizes and the generally *impulsive* or spontaneous (more probably the former) quality of his *motor executions.* These data reinforce our hypothesis that he is labile and outgoing and that he tends to act out rather than suppress the discharge of his drives. One can infer that his outgoing and assertive behavior may, perhaps, stimulate counterassertive behavior in others so that, in turn, he has more apparent external basis for his own assertiveness; hence, if this were so, he would tend to use rationalization to a pronounced degree.

Turning to an examination of the reproductions, we note that in figure A†

*The analysis of this case, done entirely on the basis of the evidence presented herewith, was originally presented at a symposium of the American Psychological Association on September 4, 1959, at Cleveland, Ohio, and later in Carr's work.[27]

†Tom numbered figure A as 1, and numbered the succeeding figures from 2 to 9. Thus, his numbering is always one digit higher than the "standard" numbering.

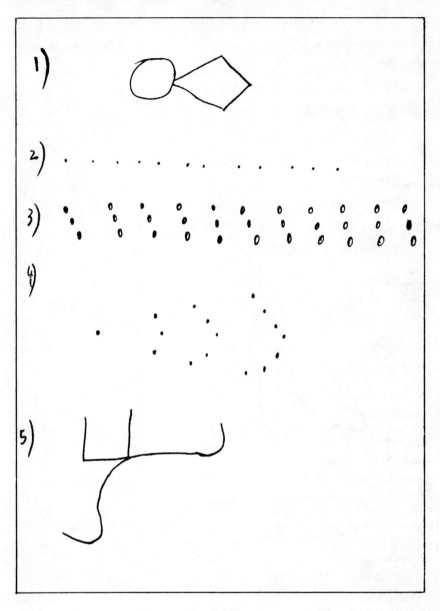

PLATE 2   Case Illustration: Tom.

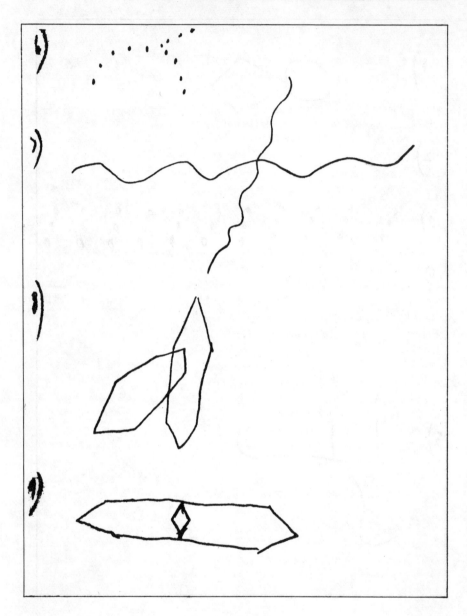

PLATE 3   Case Illustration: Tom, continued.

(the circle and the square), he *reproduces the Gestalt adequately* (this will turn out to be generally true of the other figures); he places the figure in a *common position on the page* for figure A (slightly left, top portion of the page); *enlarges the square* in proportion to the circle, *markedly increasing its horizontal dimension;* shows *impulsivity* in the drawing of the circle (overlap in closure); shows *joining difficulty* of the square and circle; makes *no attempt to correct* or erase; slightly flattens the circle, the net effect of which is to *increase the total lateral or horizontal dimension* of the figure. From these observations, we are led to the following hypotheses: he has good contact with reality, and has reasonably good ego cathexes; he tends to be conventional rather than unconventional in his social orientation; he is making considerable effort to establish or maintain interpersonal relationships (showing a need for such relationships); he tends to be fearful in authority situations; impulsivity, as a character trait, must be fairly marked; he is dissatisfied with the nature of his interpersonal relationships, and more specifically is concerned over his sexual adequacy; affect is outgoing but may lack depth and integrated qualities in his total behavior.

This exemplifies some of the methods of inducing hypotheses. Due to limitations of space, the remaining figures will be dealt with in less detail. Figure 1 does not have much to offer us. It is *correctly reproduced*, although there is some *tendency toward paired grouping* of the dots. The dots are made *fairly heavily*, but neatly (no sketching). These data support the hypotheses that Tom is in reasonably good contact with reality; he has good energy capacity which he expends in a centrifugal manner. The *increase in the laterality* of this reproduction emphasizes Tom's need to relate to others.

Figure 2 shows the following features: *initially correct angulation* of the first column of figures with a *constantly increasing egocentric orientation* of the successive columns (as if Tom were the pivot around which the columns were oriented); *correct number of columns* (if there were 11 columns in the original stimulus); circles drawn as *good loops*, but with *some impulsivity* and some *closure difficulty*. Inferences: good perceptual accuracy, but strong narcissistic tendency and generally forceful but impulsive behavior; some fearfulness in interpersonal relationships. The egocentric trend combined with the previously noted labile and outgoing qualities indicate that, as a second order inference, he is insecure but compensates rather well for his latent anxiety.

On figure 3 we note a *radical, lateral and over-all expansion* in the *size* of the figure but the *Gestalt is preserved*. However, this time the *dots are heavily filled in* (in contrast to figure 1). Thus, in an unclosed figure, Tom strives even more strongly in stressing his need for dependent interpersonal relations, but at the same time becomes more openly aggressive in his behavior.

Figure 4 gives us some additional clues to the underlying sources of Tom's problems and the residual behavior which he manifests. The unbalanced feature of this figure (with the curve at a 45 degree rotation from the horizontal) is relatively more upsetting to anxious, nonspontaneous adults than to others. In his reproduction, Tom makes two adaptations. First, he draws the curve in such a manner that the acuteness of the angle of the base and the upper curve is reduced. Second, he markedly increases the size of the curve, both absolutely and in relation to the open square. In addition, there is excessive, slightly fragmented looping on the ends of the curve. Further, one of the vertical sides of the open square is made longer and more jaggedly than the other. The open square is slightly larger than the stimulus but reduced in proportion to the curved figure. The typical signs of rapid, impulsive work habits are clearly noticeable. The inferences are, respectively: he has an excessive need for control and conformity; he expresses hostile drives more openly in emotionally tinged situations. He is, once again, showing his fearfulness of authority figures. Possibly, he has a more pronounced feminine than masculine identification.

Tom's first real indication of fairly severe inner tension and conflict seems to be revealed on figure 5. Here some very striking modifications appear in his reproduction. In the first place, the hallmark of poorly controlled, impulsive drives appears: his figure collides with the upper edge of the page, and the vertical axis of the figure is thereby *foreshortened*. Yet, he makes no attempt to correct the figure or redraw it. He decreases the number of dots in both parts of the figure, but fills each dot in very heavily. Again, let us remind ourselves that this is an open, noncontinuous figure (less structured). We cannot be sure of the possible sources of this overt, obvious breakdown in controls, but the following suggest themselves. Possibly, the accumulation of frustrations involved in the test procedure has begun to have its effect. More importantly, the unstructured quality of the figure creates special problems for an individual attempting to assert control through acting out and overcompensation. Other possibilities are, of course, likely to account for these phenomena. In any case, planning and anticipation are now shown to be inadequate. He is not the comfortable, confident figure he tries to present to the world. The tendency to edging of his figures, previously evident but not commented upon, is now reinforced by placement of the figure almost in the extreme, left-upper corner position. Strong compensatory efforts to ward off feelings of inadequacy and frustration are evident in the excessive effort devoted to filling in the very heavy dots.

On figure 6, an extreme expansion in size, in both lateral and vertical planes, is noted. The size is more than doubled in both dimensions. The curves are flattened in the horizontal plane, and made irregularly and rectangularly in the vertical plane. The angulation of the figure is generally preserved, but the figure is rotated slightly in a counterclockwise fashion. The loops, particularly at the ends of the vertical curve, are reversed. The whole figure appears to have been drawn rapidly and no revisions or corrections attempted. Inferences: acting-out tendencies, under conditions of emotional stimulation, are very pronounced; egocentrism is a central feature of the personality; contact with reality is maintained, and social conformity is exercised despite marked tendencies toward impulsivity; the extroverted, non-self critical features of the personality are highlighted. Aggresive tendencies, formerly kept under more adequate control, now assert themselves boldly.

Figure 7 shows the following features: simplification of the Gestalt (in that the two figures are made to overlap in the vertical segment of the vertical figure); closure difficulty; irregularity in line movement and line quality. We can now hypothesize that under the impact of progressive traumata there is a regressive tendency; despite initial tendencies to apparent confidence in interpersonal behavior, there is considerable conflict and fearfulness in such situations; underneath the armor of self-confidence there is considerable latent hostility.

The last figure, figure 8, is striking and unique in several respects. Despite his perceptual maturity, as revealed in previous drawings, he has considerable difficulty with this figure. The left-hand vertex of the lateral hexagon shows considerable evidence of motor incoordination and poor control; joining and closure difficulty are very noticeable; he has great difficulty with the internal diamond, doing some redrawings for the first time and making many false motor movements in the process. Despite the history of heterosexual adjustment which we are given, this analyst would question Tom's heterosexual adjustment. This reproduction is indicative of fairly marked conflict over homosexual tendencies. This problem probably lies at the core of his difficulties and insecurities in interpersonal relationships: he is really unsure of his sexual identity, and overcompensates with apparent masculine behavior to mask this problem for himself. The ambivalent quality of the internal diamond as a sexual symbol makes Tom's usual coping methods less adequate on this figure, and hence the redrawing and obvious uncertainties on this part of the reproduction. One can also hypothesize that if Tom is egocentric in orientation as we have suggested, problems centering around masturbation as a tension reducer are also present.

Our analysis has yielded several hypotheses concerning underlying source traits and several hypotheses concerning explicit and simplex examples of overt behavior. We have begun to understand Tom as an outgoing, labile, assertive individual with strong, overcompensatory characteristics. We have seen that he ordinarily holds on to an adequate perception of reality but that he shows considerable regression (neurotic in character) under specified conditions, namely, cumulative stress and, more specifically, emotional types of trauma. We have seen certain features of his attempts at control through compulsive conformity and external props. From these and other types of evidence we must try to understand why it is that he functions, at least on this test, in the unique ways that he does.

The core of his difficulties may be hypothesized to be in the problem of his sexual identity. Our inference is that he has dealt with the problem of latent homosexual tendencies by various mastery and compensatory techniques. Together with the hypothesis that he is egocentric but centrifugal in his orientation, we can point to an unsuccessfully resolved and repressed oedipal problem, with the likelihood that he was overprotected by a mother with whom he tended to identify. He had learned to perceive himself as more comfortable in a feminine role, but conflict resulting from the assumption of this role led him to assume more outgoing, assertive and "masculine" behaviors as a more secure mode of adjustment. Nevertheless, the underlying conflict remained and more compensatory mechanisms were necessary to maintain a heterosexual way of life. On the other hand, the heterosexual way of life had its own social rewards, and probably helped to differentiate him from his identical twin. Thus, the masculine ways of behaving were re-inforced and, in turn, these ways produced secondary gratification. Under-neath, infantile sexuality remained and fear of really close interpersonal relationships was fostered. Thus, his self-perception became ever more obtuse and he had to learn to bolster his own sense of self by more outgoing, masculine behavior. In the process, spontaneous affective response and capacity for mature fantasy behavior were diminished. This, then, is the neurotic character structure which is suggested by our data. Note that we are giving no attention to physical history and other biological factors which may be relevant and important in attempting to understand Tom. Were these available we could then proceed to correct and supplement our present formulation.

Assuming our basic analysis is substantially correct, what can we infer about overt behavior? Here, we are severely limited by not knowing the conditions of the testing and by not having observational data concerning Tom's methods of work, his verbalizations and the like. Nor does this accounting of shortcomings include other types of life-history and test data. However, given these limitations, what can we now infer—with, of course, lowered limits of confidence?

First, we can predict that Tom will function at least reasonably well in many, if not most, situations. He has considerable energy available for daily tasks. He gives the superficial impression of a likeable, fairly stable and assertive person. He is usually orderly and controlled enough not to be gauche and to be able to conform to social situations fairly well. His emotional behavior is also a social asset in that his outgoing and apparently labile, responsive qualities make him rather attractive to others. He would particularly appeal to masculine-oriented women who would not see him as a threat to their own masculine strivings. He would generally tend to be expansive in mood and rarely reveal depressive reactions. Neither would he easily confide to others his own gnawing feelings of inadequacy, nor would he be likely to reveal to others, much less to himself, his fearfulness of authority figures. He would be able to establish superficial relationships quite readily, and he would be a joiner and an active participant, but he would not develop intense relationships with anyone easily, if at all. Not only would he be assertive, he would be self-assertive, whenever the situation permitted. One would also predict there would be apparently inexplicable periods of indecision, work reduction, and even more overt disorganization when he was unable to escape from repetitive emotional frustration. His own self-doubts and feelings of uncertainty would finally lead him to seek some form of therapeutic help.

IV

Techniques of Administration

In its routine use, the Revised Bender-Gestalt Test is generally employed as part of a battery of psychological tests. Frequently, due to its simplicity and the fact that the RBGT is relatively nonthreatening, it is the first test administered. During the administration of this test, both the clinician and the patient can "feel each other out" and establish a suitable relationship. Because the test requires minimal interaction between the examiner and patient and because relatively little verbal interplay is called for, the patient can structure the degree and type of relationship in the manner that is most comfortable for him. Hence, some clinicians select the RBGT for administration as the first or an early test in the diagnostic battery. Later, other diagnostic procedures can be introduced more easily, as a consequence.

It is axiomatic, of course, that the patient be "prepared" for psychological testing and that an appropriate relationship be established before the test is administered. How this is done will vary with the individual clinician, but an attempt should be made to meet the needs expressed by the patient in the clinical situation, allaying anxiety, dealing with suspiciousness and giving such reassurance as is necessary. In the opinion of the authors, one of the criteria of good psychological examinations is the extent to which the examiner can help the patient to accept the test situation in terms of his own best interests and aid him in achieving the most effective use of his personality and his talents. Until this is accomplished, no formal testing should be initiated, except under very special circumstances.

In discussing the administration of the Revised Bender-Gestalt, a word should first be said concerning the physical features of the testing situation. It is advisable to have a number of medium-soft pencils available for the patient. Pencils of number 2-3 hardness have been found most satisfactory since they are not so soft as to produce a line thick enough to obscure any tremor, yet are not so hard that great pressure is required to make all lines easily visible. In addition, if the pencils are without erasers, an eraser should be made conspicuously available. It is suggested that the subject make his drawings on blank, unruled bond paper about 8½ x 11 inches in size, and that about two dozen sheets be provided and kept in view on top of the desk or table. It is important that the patient be seated comfortably and have a smooth writing surface on which to work.*

Basic Method of Administration: Adults

The routine clinical use of the full RBGT for diagnostic purposes when no special problems are anticipated is termed the basic method of administration. It consists of three phases.

The first phase of the test procedure, called the *copy phase,* may be utilized alone when the clinician needs only minimal data for clinical interpretation. This method follows:

After establishing rapport, as discussed above, the clinician introduces the specific instructions. The language to be employed in explaining the task may vary with the patient's needs and with his linguistic and intellectual abilities. The following formula will usually prove to be adequate. "I am going to show you some cards, one at a time. Each card has a simple drawing on it. I want you to copy them on the paper as well as you can. Work in any way that is best for you. This is not a test of artistic ability, but try to copy the drawings as accurately as possible. Work as fast or as slowly as you wish."

The examiner then takes a sheet of paper from the pile on the desk and places it before the patient with its long axis perpendicular to him. Any change made by the patient in the position of the paper should be noted. Card A is then presented with its base (as indicated by the letter A on the back) toward the patient, with the remark, "Copy this as well as you can." The stack of paper is constantly available for the patient's use. The patient is not permitted to use any mechanical guides (such as a straight edge for the lines or a coin for the circular or curved figures) and is told, if he asks about this, that the copying must be done freehand. All other questions about methods of work (such as amount of time to use, corrections, placement of the figure on the paper, size of the reproduction and the like) should be referred back to the patient with the comment: "Do it the way you think is best," or "That's up to you," or "There are no rules about how you should work."

It will be noted that the patient is free to use as many sheets of paper as he wishes: the significance of this will be discussed more fully later. One

---

*When the patient is given the test under unusual circumstances, these conditions will, of course, have to be approximated. Careful note should be made, however, of all such special conditions.

of the questions that sometimes arises is how to present the paper to the patient. The following suggestion may suffice. The examiner simply places a stack of paper near the patient. When the test gets started, he takes off the first sheet and places it before the patient. The patient is not permitted to draw on the top sheet while the other sheets are underneath, for obvious reasons.

The consistent avoidance of specific structuring of methods of work is regarded as most important, since it is one of the fundamental assumptions of this test procedure that the unique ways in which the patient plans for and organizes the test situation reveal some important aspects of his personality. If the patient asks how many sheets of paper he may use, he should be told something like this: "That's entirely up to you. You may use any amount you like." While some advantages may be claimed for the instruction to the patient that he draw all of the figures on one sheet (as some authorities advise), much valuable data will be lost with respect to order of arrangement and use of space if the setting is limited in this way.

When card A is completed, it is taken away and card 1 is exposed next. The same procedure is used for the remaining cards, each card being exposed in correct sequence with the base, as indicated by the number on the back, toward the patient, and each card being visible during the entire period that the patient is working on it.

The sequence in which the cards are exposed is important. It has been observed that because of perseverative and other factors, variations in the procedure will alter results.

All of the patient's comments as well as methods of work should be recorded. For a detailed analysis of an RBGT protocol, information indicating which parts of the figures were drawn first and the direction of movement is necessary. Such notations can be made directly on the work sheet by using appropriate numbers and arrows on the reproductions of the test stimuli. Particular note should be made of "blocking," "sketching," and other evidence of difficulty with a figure or part of it.

If the patient turns the card, the examiner should replace it in its original position and the patient should be encouraged to keep it in this position, with the base toward him. If he insists upon drawing it with the card in a different position, note should be made of the changed orientation of the card so that the proper interpretation may later be made of the patient's behavior and performance.

It is usually not necessary to time the performance, but note should be made if the patient takes an unduly long time with a particular figure.

The second part of the basic procedure is called the *elaboration phase*. After the *copy phase* has been completed, the drawings of the patient are removed from sight. The patient is then told: "That's fine. Now I'm going to ask you to do something else with these drawings. This time, I'd like you to modify the figures in any way that you wish so as to make them more pleasing to you. Feel free to change them in any way that you like. (They may even remind you of things.) You can change the drawings as little or as much as you like. Just make them more pleasing to yourself. Do you understand what I'd like you to do?" Any questions are then answered within the framework of these instructions.

The examiner then presents the stimulus cards in order,* leaving only the card that the patient is working on in view.† If the subject does not wish to modify a drawing, he should be told, "All right, but will you please copy it again the way it is?"

After the cards have been presented and the patient has completed his elaborations, the *association phase* is begun. Each of the stimulus cards is re-exposed in turn, alongside of the patient's elaboration of that stimulus, and the patient is asked, "Now look at the drawing on the card and at the modification you made of it. What does each of them remind you of? What could it be?" The examiner records the patient's associations to each card and its elaboration, and indicates whether the association was offered to the original stimulus or to the elaboration. If an association is offered to the stimulus or to the elaboration only, the patient is asked to offer an association to the other part. It is advisable to number the associations sequentially for each figure. Also note the patient's explanation of the basis for his associations.

The basic method of administering the RBGT discussed above has the following rationale. First, the *copy phase* presents a standardized testing situation with regard to the way in which the test is introduced as well as to the materials and their manner of presentation to the patient. This, of course, is necessary if any meaningful interpretations, research, and interchange of information among clinicians are to be carried out. However, within these broad limits, the patient is free to structure the task in any way that he sees fit. He is presented with a pencil, eraser, and batch of paper and is literally told nothing else about the procedure. All of his questions are referred back to him with the comment, essentially, "Do it the way you think is best." Thus, the patient is encouraged to organize the task in his own unique manner and to project into the "space" of the test situation his own conscious and un-

---

*If it is desired to reduce the total time required for this test, it is recommended that only cards A, 2, 4, 6, 7 and 8 be administered for this phase of the examination. Usually, these cards provide an adequate sample of all the data that are needed.

†This procedure may be modified so as to shorten the total time for administration. See page 107ff.

conscious needs. His planning and organizing behavior reflects many aspects of the ways in which he characteristically reacts in real life; i.e., his personal style.

The *elaboration* and *association phases* of the basic method give the clinician additional opportunity to observe the manner in which the patient behaves. In these phases of the test, the patient is presented with a relatively ambiguous task and is asked to deal with it in some meaningful way. The manner in which he changes or refuses to change his responses to the stimuli, and his association to the original stimuli and to his own drawings allow the clinician to evaluate the symbolic value the stimuli have for the patient, the need systems that are being expressed, and consistency in patterns of behavior.

Even when general methods of work and types of responses to the figures are consistent in the *copy* and *elaboration phases* of the test, patients vary in their freedom to deviate from the original stimulus as well as in the amount of distortion they may manifest. It should be pointed out that, when used in this manner, the RBGT is not nearly as ambiguous as the Rorschach inkblots, but is more ambiguous than TAT type tests. The same projective processes that operate in these tests also operate in the RBGT.

Other Methods of Administration

A wide variety of variation in methods of administration may be utilized to meet special clinical conditions or problems. We shall discuss several major types of adaption and discuss, briefly, some possible uses for them.

Tachistoscopic method. When intracranial pathology is suspected, the following tachistoscopic technique of administration is recommended.*

Although the RBGT is essentially innocuous and relatively non-emotionally charged for most clinical patients, it may be intensely threatening to individuals with neurologic deficits since it involves the very areas of functioning in which organic patients experience greatest difficulty. For this reason, the utmost care should be exercised in obtaining rapport and preparing these patients for testing.

The test materials and their arrangement are substantially the same as for the basic method of administration. The patient is told in substance: "Now I'm going to show you some cards that have designs drawn on them. I shall let you look at each one for only a few seconds. Then I'll take it away and ask you to draw it from memory. Do you understand what I want you to do?" Any questions by the patient are then answered,

---

*Of course, the *basic method* may also be employed for such patients. The special method that is suggested here will help to maximize the psychological effects, if any, of brain damage.

Card A is then exposed by placing it on the table in front of the patient for a period of five seconds. It is then removed. After the patient completes his drawing, card 1 is similarly presented, and the procedure is repeated for the remaining cards. The patient is free, of course, to use as much paper as he desires, but experience indicates that almost all patients tend to place all of their tachistoscopic reproductions on one sheet. Care should be exercised to keep from distracting the patient during this administration. After all nine cards have been presented, the patient's drawings are removed from sight. The cards may then be readministered in the *copy phase* of the *basic method*, if desired.

Reproduction from memory. The procedure to test the patient's reproduction of the RBGT figures from memory must follow the basic *copy phase*. When the patient completes Figure 8 of the *copy phase*, the original cards and drawings are removed. He is then told: "Now I would like you to draw as many of the designs as you can remember."

Some patients may attempt to get clues from the examiner about the correctness of their reproductions, or they may ask whether they have recalled all of the figures, saying, "That's right, isn't it?" or "I guess that's all of them, huh?" The best replies to the questions such as these have been found to follow this general line: "I'm sorry, but I'm not permitted to tell you." "Do it the way you think is best and decide for yourself."

At the conclusion of the memory phase, if further information is desired, the clinician can then continue testing with the *elaboration* and *association phases* of the basic method of administration.

These tachistoscopic and memory methods of administration are particularly effective in cases of organic brain damage because they are a means of varying the temporal factor in perception, which is of considerable importance in cases of organic deficit. All normal perception takes place within certain temporal limits. Normals tend to experience primitive perceptual forms when a stimulus is given very rapid exposures. However, the brain-injured tend to experience primitive forms on even moderately long stimulus presentations. By presenting the RBGT stimuli tachistoscopically a temporal factor is introduced into the testing situation, and the differences from the *copy phase* in the form-level of the reproduction may provide additional data to enable the clinician more easily to discriminate patients with organic brain damage from non-brain damaged patients.

Use of the tachistoscopic and memory techniques of administration for the RBGT are also indicated in certain forms of early schizophrenia. When the schizophrenic patient has remnants of previous rigid defenses intact, he is sometimes able to "hold on" (in the copy phase) to the stimulus figures so that his reproductions of them are without severe distortions. Tachistoscopic administration to this kind of patient has much the same effect it has with organic patients. The temporal interval tends to reduce the effectiveness of the defensive maneuvers and permits the schizophrenic disturbances of perception and association to become more readily apparent.

The *memory phase* of the RBGT administration is also useful with most clinical patients. In dealing with this additional memory material, two general assumptions are made: (1) Material which has had a traumatic impact upon the patient will either tend to be repressed, if it has been too disturbing, or will tend to be reproduced first (or early) in the recall sequence, if it is unpleasant but the patient feels he can discharge some of his anxiety in "working it through." (2) The patient will tend to exaggerate his previous distortions (or maintain the same degree of distortion) for those figures which were moderately to severely disturbing, while he will make compensatory adjustments for those previously distorted figures (and the related psychological phenomena) on which his performance was marginal. A corollary to these assumptions is that to the extent that the patient suffers from more severe psychopathology, he will make more errors in recall (fail to retain the figures) and make more serious distortions then on the original reproductions. It is also assumed that the total amount of retention is positively correlated with the patient's level of general intelligence. Thus, analysis of the recall material enables confirmation, or rejection, of inferences previously established for the reproductions obtained by the *basic method*, and offers additional sources of data concerning other aspects of the patient's performance and personality characteristics.

Testing the limits. Another variation in the administration procedure may prove useful in making more effective differential diagnoses between some types of schizophrenic patients and organic patients. This is a kind of *testing the limits* designed to clarify and elucidate the nature of the patient's perceptions and his ability to make changes as he reperceives the original stimulus and compares it with his reproduction. This *testing the limits* should be carried out after all other phases of the RBGT administration have been completed.

Testing the limits is indicated when such major distortions as rotation, reversal, simplification, elaboration, and the like occur. When such records are obtained, and a difficult diagnostic problem is anticipated, the original stimulus card is re-presented to the patient and he is asked to compare it with his own reproduction to see "whether they are alike." If the patient becomes aware of the discrepancy between his drawing and the stimulus, he is asked to make another copy on a fresh sheet of paper. Should the patient

be unable to perceive the discrepancy, he may be told that there is a difference and is asked to try very hard to find it. If no awareness of the distortion appears, appropriate note should be made and the issue dropped. If
some awareness does occur, the nature of the reaction can be noted for later
evaluation. Clinical experience indicates that the organic patient has great
difficulty in noting discrepancies involving rotation and reversal, and if
finally he does become aware of them, he may be unable to specify what
the distortion involves. Further, he will usually be unable to reproduce the
stimulus accurately on a second attempt. The schizophrenic, on the other
hand, unless severely deteriorated, will, with difficulty, be able to see the
discrepancy and he will be able to make an adequate correction or improve
upon his initial performance.

Another form of *testing the limits* may prove helpful when a patient
approaches the task in a nonchalant, haphazard manner. Such patients are
usually "unwilling subjects" and are often seen in penal or court settings,
or are persons who have little or no personal motivation or involvement in
testing. Frequently, the drawings of such a patient are grossly distorted and
the question of whether or not serious pathology is present is raised. On
other occasions the distortions that appear in a protocol may seem out of all
proportion to the clinical impression of the patient. And, finally, patients are
seen who consciously attempt to appear far sicker than they actually are. In
such cases as these, the forced copy technique of Bender-Gestalt administration may prove helpful.

When such a protocol is obtained from the basic method of administration,
all planned testing should be completed. If possible, for best results several
days should elapse before seeing the patient again. When the patient is next
seen, the *copy phase* of the RBGT should be readministered. Often this
second *copy phase* may prove sufficient to clarify the issues, since the elapsed
time may have induced the patient to forget the specific distortions he made
on the original test and, consequently, there will be considerable discrepancies
between the two tests. If further elucidation is desired, the patient is then
shown his latest copy and the stimulus figure and asked, "Does yours look
like this?" The examiner must then take the patient's reply as his cue for
further questioning. The examiner can ask the patient to identify the specific
elements of the original stimulus, compare his reproductions with them, and
finally the examiner can ask the patient to attempt to improve his reproductions. "Try to make it look just like that," or "You can do better than that,"
or "You don't even seem to be trying."

A word of caution must be offered in connection with this technique. Before it is attempted, every other means should be taken to determine how
much conscious distortion is present in the test data. If the readministered
copy phase answers the question, that should be sufficient. The indiscriminate

use of this *forced copy technique* with clinical patients can lead to difficulty since it is damaging to rapport and may evoke considerable hostility on the part of the patient. In any case in which it is used, only as much pressure as is necessary to get the required information should be employed.

Methods of Administration with Children

When the RBGT is used with children, several modifications may be necessary. Use of the test is not usually recommended for children who are less than seven years of age, since they have not reached the maturational level necessary to draw adequately all of the figures.[4]

When children are tested, it has been found to be best to structure the situation as a game. The *copy phase* can be presented as follows: "Now we're going to play a drawing game. I'll show you cards that have pictures on them and I want you to copy them the best you can." It may be necessary to use some slight encouragement, "That's fine, now let's try this one." Otherwise, the procedure is the same as for adults, although questions that the child asks may be referred back with the comment, "Try to do it the way *you* think is best." Where necessary, approbation may be given.

Other phases of the test may be given when necessary. The examiner is cautioned to remember that children become restless and have shorter interest and attention spans than adults, and for these reasons testing sessions should be kept as brief as possible. Furthermore, greater distortions than are common to adults are to be expected on tachistoscopic administration since the child has not reached full maturational development and so will have more difficulty organizing the temporal factors in perception than do adolescents or adults.

When special clinical problems arise with respect to the test management of difficult patients, variations from the testing procedures outlined above may be made. When this is the case, special note should be taken since these variations must be considered during interpretation. The interpretive schema to be described in subsequent chapters is based upon data obtained from the standardized administration and any variations from this administration may influence the validity of the interpretation.

It may be desirable in certain instances to use the RBGT in group testing as a screening device or for research purposes. Projection of the designs by lantern slide has been found to be most satisfactory. However, data obtained from such a presentation will not be suitable, for obvious reasons, for interpretation regarding size of figure and sequence.

Within the limits suggested above, the RBGT can be adapted to a wide variety of clinical uses and permits great flexibility in approaching specific problems that patients may present.

V

Specific Test Factors and Their Interpretation

In this chapter we shall present a summary of the specific test factors which have been found useful in interpreting response to the RBGT, together with definitions of the factors and their probable clinical significance. We shall reserve for Chapter VI a discussion of the principles of configurational analysis, the symbolic value of the various figures, and methods of dealing with consistencies and inconsistencies in the total test record, including the *associational* and *elaborational phases*.

A number of introductory observations may be in order first. The interpretative or predictive values suggested in the following presentation apply specifically to "adult" records. This is not to say that they may not, in some cases, be applicable to children's records,[6,7] but we are focusing emphasis on variables pertinent to "adult" cases.* By "adult" record is meant a record obtained from an individual 18 or more years of age. In such records we have reasonable assurance that the distortions in Gestalten or difficulties in organizational and line movement qualities are not attributable to inadequacies in biological maturation.

The clinician must also be reasonably certain that distortions of the Gestalten or disturbances in line quality are not attributable to factors extraneous to the patient, such as errors or imperfections in the stimulus figures, rough or irregular surface on which the drawings are made, or improper pencil for drawing.

Each of the factors discussed below is related to certain personality processes or outcomes. The examiner begins by assuming that the presence of a particular factor has the meaning (or meanings) assigned to it. As he pro-

---

*See Chapter XIII for a discussion of children's records.

ceeds in his analysis of a particular record he may develop alternate or modified hypotheses concerning the significance of a factor as it is repeated, occurs in new configurations, or has some unique attributes not covered by our definitions (see Chapter VI). Thus, the process of interpretation is guided by the typical meanings of the several factors and is subsequently refined on the basis of confirmatory or contradictory evidence. It will be seen that in those scoring schemes based on the cumulative value of a particular type of distortion or upon the total frequency of all types of distortions, only the typical meaning of a distortion is considered.

It is not assumed that the present list of factors includes all of the possibly pertinent variables. We have included only those factors which in the light of persistent findings in clinical work or in the light of pertinent research evidence may be presumed to be significant. Nor is it assumed that our definitions are optimal. Further evidence may, and probably will, suggest modification in this respect also.

Finally, a word of caution is offered. The presence of a single factor, no matter how blatant or extreme its manifestation, hardly justifies a diagnostic conclusion about the patient—although it may warrant the status of a strong hypothesis. Diagnosis should rest on more substantial grounds, such as congruent evidence from a number of sources or repetitive evidence from a single source.

The summary of test factors is categorized into five major groupings: Organization, Size, Changes in Form, Gross Distortion, and Movement.

Factors Relating to Organization

Organizational factors refer to the methods by which the patient organizes and places his drawings on the sheet or sheets of paper. Such factors tell us, in general, something of how the patient conceives and utilizes his "life space." Since he is free to use one or more sheets of paper, to crowd or spread his drawings, to arrange his drawings logically in sequence or otherwise, his resultant behavior on the tests tells us something of how he relates himself to the world around him. Sometimes we may catch a glimpse of these organizational processes at work, as the patient methodically plans each figure placement before he begins to draw, or as he impulsively starts to place a figure in an inappropriate space and then changes his placement. Other times, an inspection of these aspects of the record uncovers the meaning of these resultants in behavior, as when a highly suspicious and fearful patient has placed all of his drawings in a small section of the upper half of one sheet of paper, or when he "crowds" all of his drawings against the margin of the paper.

1. *Sequence*

This refers to the successive positions of the drawings as they are reproduced by the patient on the page. For example, some patients start at about the middle of the page, near the top, and place the subsequent drawings in a straight line going down the middle of the page. Other patients will start near the upper left corner of the page, next move across the page on a horizontal line, then go back to the left-hand side of the page and proceed again to the right on a straight line, etc. Other patients, usually those who are more disturbed, will show a much more irregular sequence. They may start at any point on the page and scatter their remaining drawings in a haphazard and unplanned manner.

Sequence, as manifested in the RBGT records, may be characterized as: overly methodical, methodical, irregular, confused or symbolic.

a. *Overly methodical sequence.* The patient places his drawings in a fixed sequence, never deviating from the sequence in his placement of any of the figures, maintaining undeviating rigidity in his approach. For example, the patient may start in the upper left-hand corner and then place the subsequent drawings directly on the left-hand margin of the paper, always starting them against the margin and not changing from this procedure until he has moved all the way down to the bottom of the page, at which time he may then move to the right-hand side of the page and use the right-hand margin for the remaining figures. A rigid sequence can usually be determined easily by inspection by virtue of the fact that the placement of the drawings seems forced and does not take into account the actual shape or characteristics of the figures, characteristics which would ordinarily lead the patient to shift the figure to a more appropriate position even though this might change the order or sequence slightly.

Summary criterion: No deviation from a fixed, rigid sequence, despite the obvious requirements of the stimulus and despite the space available on the page.

b. *Methodical sequence.* One in which the patient follows a regular succession throughout his production of the drawings. *No more than two exceptions or changes in direction is allowed.* The succession of drawings may be from left to right or from top to bottom or may follow some other simple and logical arrangement.

Summary criterion: No more than two deviations in sequence of successive placement of drawings. Deviation is defined as a change in the placement of the next figure from the sequence which followed just previously. Example: The following placements of figures A to 8 represents two changes in sequence, indicated by the X's and arrows in the accompanying chart.

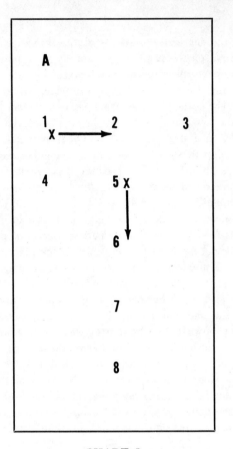

CHART 1.

c. *Irregular sequence.* One in which more than two changes in direction is evident, but no obvious confusion in sequence can be detected. For example, the patient may start at the left-hand side of the page, and then move to the right, then start going down for the next drawing (this is the first change in sequence), then change his course again and start at the left, moving from that point to the right (this is his third inversion). Although the patient shows more than two changes of direction, it is still possible to determine by inspection the logic or change of logic in his sequence.

Summary criterion: More than two deviations in sequence, but no obvious confusion.

d. *Confused or symbolic sequence.* This is characterized by a jumble or lack of any apparent plan by which the drawings are placed on the page.

This sequence is most frequently found in the case of psychotics who are actively disturbed, and less frequently in the case of patients who are suffering from intense and overwhelming anxiety.

There is a special kind of sequence which may be observed occasionally to which the authors have attached the label "symbolic." For example, one patient arranged his drawings in such a way that they followed the configuration of the figure 8. This type of sequence may, on inspection, reveal some plan, but is highly unusual and has a special, symbolic meaning for the patient. Other symbolic sequences more frequently seen are circular or rectangular in style.

Summary criterion: A sequence without any apparent logic, or one which has some symbolic significance for the patient.

In general, the sequence that the patient employs tells us something about his methods of intellectual functioning, as well as the nature of his ego functions. The more rigid the sequence, the more rigid and overcontrolled is his intellectual functioning. Normal patients will usually manifest methodical and occasionally an irregular sequence. Some individuals who are compulsive but might still be classified as normally adjusted may show an overly methodical sequence, although this sequence is more frequently found among neurotics who utilize compulsive defenses.

The way in which the ego controls behavior, making it overly rigid or encouraging spontaneity of functioning, is important in the total evaluation of the personality, and it is for this reason that, in the analysis of a test record, sequence is considered very early in the process of interpretation (see Chapter VI). Confused sequence is characteristic of a severely disturbed ego and consequently is usually found in the protocols of patients with severe reactive conditions, such as delirium, dissociative and toxic psychosis, and in those patients with a "fragmented" ego such as process schizophrenia.[26]

Sequence is also an indicator of the patient's judgment or planning ability. This is another characteristic of the degree of ego function available to the patient. The patient who places a figure on the page in such a way that there is insufficient room for it so that he is forced to distort it in some manner is manifesting a deficiency in ego function. The patient with a healthy ego is able to execute a well-placed, well-planned and undistorted figure. At the other extreme is the patient whose reproduction of the stimulus figure is broken and continued on another page or continued in the space immediately below the initial drawing.

Also important to interpretation is the point at which the sequence changes. Some patients, for example, begin with an orderly sequence for the first few drawings, but when they approach the bottom of the paper they cram the remaining figures into the bottom of the page or perhaps scatter them in a disorganized manner in whatever space remains on the page. This behavior implies that the individual may function superficially in a reasonable fashion but is at a borderline level of integration and may regress quite rapidly under tension or trauma. Psychological concomitants of such test behavior include rigidity with low frustration tolerance, high latent anxiety, indecisiveness and compulsive doubting, and covert feelings of inadequacy. The specific explanation for any particular patient can be determined only on the basis of other factors in his test behavior or on the basis of other clinical findings.

Sudden changes in the former pattern of sequential progression may indicate impulsivity or a reaction to the symbolic meaning of the figure at which the change in sequence occurred.

Sequential progression from right to left suggests negativism or a cultural background that is deviant from the American mores. Progression from the bottom to the top of the page is indicative of even more severe negativistic trends.

If more than one sheet of paper is used, the sequential arrangements may still be characterized on the basis of the classification we have suggested.

In general, unselected patients most frequently use one or occasionally two sheets of paper. Use of more than two sheets of paper is in itself quite unusual and in the experience of the authors occurs in the case of some psychopathic personalities who will use a separate sheet of paper for each figure. Such an arrangement has as its psychological concomitants narcissism, egocentricity and expansiveness. Other clinical groups in which such an arrangement may occasionally be seen are manics and grandiose schizophrenics. Differential diagnosis is, of course, dependent upon other significant test factors.

Occasionally a patient will complete several of the drawings on the face of a sheet of paper and then turn the paper over to complete his drawings on the other side. This behavior suggests the anal characteristic of parsimony. Another sequential arrangement which is seen occasionally involves placement of the first figure, enlarged in size, in the center of the page with the remaining figures crowded around the first one. The sequence may meet the criteria of "irregular" or "confused." Such test behavior suggests marked egocentrism or narcissism in an individual with a facade of potency or security. If the first figure is reduced in size but is the center or pivot for the other figures, feelings of impotency are likely to be overwhelming.

Sequence is also important is estimating the patient's intellectual level. In well-adjusted adult subjects the presence of confused sequence is almost always associated with retarded intellectual functioning. Persons of average or better intelligence almost always utilize a methodical sequence. When an overly methodical sequence appears in a record that is otherwise not remarkable with respect to personality disturbance, it suggests average intelligence or better which is, however, inhibited by anal features in the personality.

Persons with intracranial pathology who are overcompensating often utilize an overly methodical sequence.

Research evidence indicates that sequence is related to emotional adjustment. Byrd[6] found that well-adjusted children tended to use an orderly sequence in their arrangement of RBGT figures, whereas a chaotic (confused) sequence occurred exclusively in the records of children independently diagnosed as needing therapy. On the other hand, irregular sequence tended to occur more frequently in the records of disturbed children but not at a statistically significant level. These findings, in general, are replicated by Clawson.[7] She found that sequence significantly discriminated emotionally disturbed children from a control group of well-adjusted children.

2. *Position of the First Drawing*

The meaning of this organizational category is probably self-explanatory. In general, the position selected for placement of the first figure is indicative of the patient's orientation toward the test situation and to his life-space as well. It is related to the general orientation of the patient to "his world."

About two-thirds of "unselected" adult subjects place the first drawing in the center and slightly below the top edge of the paper. The typical placement of the first drawing of these normal subjects is in a rectangular area starting about an inch from the left side and about an inch below the top margin and extending over to the right to about a similar position with respect to the right margin and going down approximately two inches. The second most frequent placement of the first drawing is in the upper left-hand corner of the paper with some margin allowed around the drawing. The third most frequent position is approximately in the center of the paper, while other positions less frequent in occurrence are at the upper right-hand corner, middle portion on the left margin or scattered positions over the remaining portions of the paper.

Analysis of clinical data indicates that placement of the first figure is correlated, generally, with approach–avoidance to life situations, as a general trait. Timid and fearful individuals tend to place their drawings in the upper left-hand corner of the paper and frequently, as another one of their characteristics, reduce the size of their drawing in comparison with the stimulus. Narcissistic, egocentric, and psychopathic individuals more frequently place their first drawing in the middle of the paper and often enlarge the size of the figure. Any atypical or bizarre position for the first drawing is always suspect, and while it may occasionally represent a transient reaction to intense anxiety, it is more frequently representative of a profound disturbance in personality organization. Placement of figure A in the lower right-hand corner of the page, for example, almost invariably is indicative of eccentricity, anxiety, and ego disturbance of psychotic proportions.

Summary criteria: a. *Normal placement:* in an area defined by a rectangle within the *upper one-third* of the page, and not closer than one inch to either the left or right margin. The typical placement is usually off-center to the left of the center of the page.

b. *Abnormal placements:* in other areas of the page, such as "hugging" the edge, in the very center of the page, and in lower left or right corners.

3. *Use of Space, I*

This factor refers to the amount of space between *any two successive drawings* on the test. In general, excessive use of space is related to expansive, aggressive modes of adaptation to life situations, while constricted use of space is related to withdrawn, covertly hostile and passive modes of adaptation.

Analysis of our data has suggested the following definitions for the amount of space between successive figures. Although these "norms" are not entirely adequate in the case of individuals who modify the size of their drawings excessively, either by increasing or decreasing size, they will be found useful in most areas.

a. *Excessive use of space.* The space between any two successive figures, in either vertical or horizontal sequence, as drawn on the page, is *more than half the size* of the corresponding axis of either figure.

b. *Constricted use of space.* The space between any two successive figures, as drawn on the page, is less than *one-fourth of the size* of the corresponding axis of either figure.

c. *Normal use of space.* Less space used than (a) above, and more than (b) above.

An excessive amount of space between successive drawings as the typical pattern for the test is indicative of strong, overt, hostile strivings. Such records indicate, at least, strong assertive and acting-out tendencies. Aggressive and rebellious individuals usually show excessive use of space. On the other hand, a constricted use of space is indicative of repressed hostility, occasionally turned inward in the form of masochistic strivings or needs. Such records characterize individuals who are withdrawn.

In short, the individual's use of space is thought to be characteristic of his attitudinal orientation toward the world around him, of whether he regards the world as a hostile or friendly place; and whether he is able to express his hostility or has to repress or suppress it. In the case of the actively paranoid individual, for example, the most common characteristic with respect to the use of space is the excessive space together with a decrease in the size of drawings and the utilization of only a small portion of the page for all of the drawings. The drawings appear to be compressed on the page and a large amount of white space appears between successive drawings. In a literal sense, the paranoid has withdrawn from the world which he regards as menacing and hostile. Other findings indicate that persons with very strict superegos tend to reduce the size of their figures, place all of the drawings in a small portion of the page and leave a lot of unused space on the page but little space between drawings; the psychopath, in contrast, uses lots of paper and has considerable amount of white space around each of his figures on the various pages which he uses. Figures spaced one to a page, however, may also suggest that the individual uses the defense mechanism of isolation.

Clawson's study[7] indicates that the use of space, as previously suggested by Hutt,[24] does significantly predict emotional disturbance and that excessive and constricted use of space are related in children, respectively, to expansive or acting-out modes of adaptation and withdrawn modes.

Use of Space, II

Normally, adult patients use one to one and two-thirds sheets to complete their drawings. Occasionally, patients will use far less or far more paper. It is possible to evaluate the use of space in terms of the total amount of pages used to reproduce the drawings. In general, withdrawn, fearful and covertly hostile patients tend to use far less than the normal amount of paper. Conversely, overly assertive, rebellious, aggressive patients use far more. As we have noted, egocentric patients may use a separate page for each drawing, increasing its size and placing it in the center of the page.

We shall discuss, in Chapter VI, various configurations in test factors in which combinations of use of space together with other factors give us fairly specific leads to the nature of the patient's inner conflicts and the methods of coping with such conflicts.

Summary criteria: A record may be characterized as showing excessive use of space if criterion (a), above, is present *two or more times*. Similarly, a record may be characterized as showing constricted use of space if criterion (b), above, is present *two or more times*.

4. Collision

This factor is related to the one above and may represent an extreme condition of the former factor. Collision refers to the tendency of figures to overlap or actually to collide. As might be inferred from previous discussion, collision is related to the continuum of acceptance and rejection. More specifically, it is indicative of the patient's present planning capacity and is, there-fore, an index of his current ego strength. Individuals who manifest an actual collision between successive drawings or even a collision tendency, that is, a near collision, almost always show a marked disturbance in ego function. The outstanding example of this sort is the case of the individual with signifi-cant psychological disturbance resulting from brain damage. In the case of actively disturbed or deteriorating psychotics, this sign is also sometimes present. Moreover, impulsive and hostile individuals who have a tendency to act out will often manifest collision tendencies and actual collisions. It is important to differentiate such individuals from those who are actively psychotic or brain-damaged. Such differential diagnosis may be aided by a consideration of many other aspects of the test record, as well as the patient's clinical behavior. (See Chaper VI.)

Summary criteria: Collision refers to the actual running together and overlapping of a figure with any other figure. Collision tendency refers to the patient's placement of a figure within $1/4$ inch of any of the other figures on his drawing.

5. *Use of the Margin*

This refers to the tendency to place the drawings along the margin of the paper. Excessive use of the margin is indicated when the patient places any portion of at least seven of his nine figures within $1/4$ inch of any of the edges of the paper. Clinical findings indicate that such an individual very fre-quently tends to manifest considerable internal tension, perceives himself as being inadequate, and has a considerable amount of anxiety, although this anxiety may not be manifested at an overt level. Frequently, individuals manifesting signs of organic brain damage will utilize the margins in order to orient their drawings on the paper. When this behavior is found in a record that is suggestive of organic brain damage, it may be interpreted as compensatory attempts by the patient to gain some control. Although the features associated with excessive use of the margin noted above are found in records of adult patients, they probably do not have similar interpretive significance in children's records.[7]

Summary criterion: Placement of seven or more of the figures within $1/4$ inch of any of the edges of the paper constitutes use of the margin.

6. *Shift in the Position of the Paper*

This factor should not be confused with the factor called *rotation* which will be discussed later. The shift factor refers to the patient's rotation of the paper more than, or at least as much as, 90 degrees from the original posi-tion in which the paper was presented to him. As will be recalled, the paper is presented to the patient so that its long axis is at right angles to his body.

Rotation of the paper of 90 degrees or more on its initial presentation is almost always found among individuals who are both egocentric and rigid in makeup. A rotation of the paper of 180 degrees or more is strongly indicative of marked oppositional tendencies, although, again, these tendencies may not be expressed in overt behavior. Patients manifesting severe anxiety or hypomanic conditions will frequently shift the paper not only on its original presentation but also on successive drawings. Very pedantic or "fussy" individuals also have strong tendencies to shift the paper for successive drawings, rotating it so they can draw all the lines in their reproduction using only horizontal or only vertical strokes of the pencil.

Summary criterion: Rotation of the paper by the patient, on its initial presentation, of at least 90 degrees.

7. *Shift in the Position of the Stimulus Cards*

This refers to the patient's turning of the cards from the position in which they were presented originally. It is found among anxious patients and those with strong oppositional tendencies. Patients who have conflict with authority figures also show this phenomena.

Summary criterion: Shifting the stimulus card so that its axis is turned 90 degrees or more from the position in its original presentation.

Factors Relating to Size

It may be noted that the patient may modify the size of a figure without in any way changing its Gestalt or otherwise distorting it. For interpretation, the examiner must simultaneously consider both the changes in size as well as the presence of other deviant manifestations.

8. *Over-All Increase or Decrease in Size of the Figures*

A design is considered as either increased or decreased when its axis, in either vertical or horizontal direction, is increased or decreased more than one-fourth of the size of the corresponding axis in the stimulus. Over-all increase or decrease is defined as an increase or decrease in size of the majority of the figures, i.e., five or more. When the patient manifests an over-all increase in size, we may conclude that he is showing a reaction formation to marked feelings of anxiety or inadequacy and impotence. This may be one of his means of denying anxiety and his overt behavior may involve boastfulness, excessive aspiration level, assertiveness or related manifestations. Frequently, he appears as the "hale fellow well met," the carefree extrovert. An over-all decrease in size of the designs is correlated with the presence of active and overt anxiety as well as overt manifestations of feelings of inadequacy, tendencies toward withdrawal, and marked impotence.

In the latter case, it is likely that the patient is experiencing conflictual demands against which he has been unable to defend himself and to which he attempts to adjust through the use of "Caspar Milquetoast" mechanisms. Two other conditions in which over-all decrease in size is present may be noted. Patients, such as obsessives and compulsives, who use the mechanisms of isolation and withdrawal frequently show this phenomenon. Some patients who are markedly disturbed and whose egos have become fragmented[26] will occasionally reveal the phenomenon of *micropsia* in which the drawings are very markedly reduced in size. In general then, at the behavioral level, over-all increase in size is related to outgoing, assertive behavior, while over-all decrease in size is related to withdrawing, passive behavior trends.

Summary criteria: An increase or decrease of the drawings in at least one axis by more than one-fourth of the corresponding axis of the stimulus figure is necessary to qualify as a change in size. Over-all increase or decrease in size is scored if changes are present in at least five drawings.

9. *Progressive Increase or Decrease in Size*

This refers to the tendency to make each successive figure either larger or smaller than the preceding one. In either case, that is, whether the figures tend to get larger or whether they tend to get smaller, this is good evidence of low frustration tolerance and acting-out tendencies. Such individuals are likely to be characteristically irritable, explosive, and even dangerous. In the case of progressive increase in size these factors are apt to be more prevalent. In general, such individuals can be characterized as extroverted personalities.

On the other hand, when there is progressive decrease in size, the individuals are more likely to be introverted personalities, who will tend to utilize repressive and suppressive defenses against their tendencies to lose control. Often, somatic complaints are present. Whether tendencies toward explosive outbursts erupt in overt behavior depends on the over-all ego strength of such patients, i.e., the stronger the ego, the less the potential of acting out. Such persons may also develop dissociative reactions.

Summary criteria: Sequential and progressive increase (or decrease) in the size of the drawings, *by any amount,* in at least six of the nine drawings meets the criterion for this factor.

10. *Isolated Increase or Decrease in Size*

Clinical findings suggest that increase or decrease in the size of a particular design or part of a design, particularly if it is out of line with the characteristics of the size of other designs, is indicative of the symbolic expression of conflict of the subject. It is well to pay special attention to the types of exaggeration or diminution in the designs which the subject makes. Most frequently, sexual disturbances are manifest in these types of modifications in size. In addition to the more obvious aspects of disturbance in phallic looking designs, changes in size may occur in the vertical plane in designs having a general vertical orientation, or in the lateral plane in the designs which are wider than they are high. In the former case, we look for evidence of some kind of difficulty in relation to authority figures. In the latter, we suspect difficulty in forming or maintaining adequate inter-personal relations and cathexes.[28]

This factor is of special importance in test protocols in which all but one of the test figures are of uniform size. Sudden changes in size of a particular figure may point directly at a specific conflict.

There is some research evidence[6,7] to indicate that increase or decrease of size in the reproduction of RBGT figures is significantly related to emotional disturbance.

Summary criterion: An increase (or decrease) in size of part of a figure or of a whole figure is judged to be present if the part is changed by more than one-quarter of the dimensions used in the rest of that figure or the whole figure is changed by a similar amount in relation to preceding or subsequent drawings.

Factors Relating to Changes in the Form of the Gestalt

11. *Closure Difficulty*

This refers to difficulty in bringing the joinings of parts of a design together. For example, in the case of design A, the patient may find it difficult to bring the end of his circular sweep together with the beginning of that sweep, so that he may show an overlap at the point of junction or an excessive amount of drawings at that point. On the same drawing, he may have difficulty in joining the circle with the square and again may manifest this by overlapping of the two designs or an excessive amount of drawing at the point of junction. Or, conversely, the closure difficulty may be evident in failure to complete a joining, i.e., a "gap."

Closure difficulty is correlated specifically with fearfulness in interpersonal relationships. Psychologically, it seems to represent an inability to maintain constant cathexes with appropriate objects in the environment. When closure difficulty is evidenced by "gaps," such distortions suggest attempts at withdrawal. On the other hand, occasionally one part of the Gestalt is intruded into the other; this suggests markedly passive, dependent needs.

The studies of Clawson[7] and Byrd,[6] cited above, indicate that closure difficulty occurs significantly more often in the test protocols of emotionally disturbed than well-adjusted children. Clinical evidence supports the other hypotheses noted above.

Summary criterion: Difficulty in the joinings of parts of a design, such as "gaps," erasures, overwork of the lines, increased pressure at the juncture, and the like, constitute this determinant.

12. *Crossing Difficulty*

This refers to difficulty, manifest in the drawing, at points where one line crosses another. The presence of this sign is indicative of psychological blocking, and is usually related to difficulties in interpersonal relationships. It is correlated with abulia, indecision, compulsive doubting, and specific phobias. It is one of the characteristics of the so-called psychasthenic individual.

Story,[37] in a study of RBGT factors in the test records of alcoholics, reasoned that the alcoholic's psychological blocking in interpersonal relationship would be manifested by crossing difficulty on figure 6. This prediction was substantiated at a high level of statistical significance.

Byrd[6] also found that crossing difficulty (he labeled this factor overlapping difficulty) was significantly related to emotional disturbance in children.

Summary criterion: Any difficulty such as redrawing, sketching, and the like, at the point of line crossings in any figure, and especially in figures 6 and 7, indicates crossing difficulty.

13. *Curvature Difficulty*

In general, curved designs seem to represent an emotional stimulus to the patient. By change in curvature is meant an increase or decrease in the rectangularity in curvature of the patient's reproduction of the design. This may be manifest in the following characteristics: flattening of curves, increase in wave amplitude, spiking of curves, irregularity in the smooth flow of the curve, change in total size of the curve.

When a patient increases the amount of curvature we take this to be indicative of an over-response to an emotional stimulus. Similarly, when the patient decreases the amount of curvature, that is, makes the designs more nearly rectangular, we take this to be an indication of suppression of affect or insensitivity to emotional stimulation from without. Our findings indicate that emotionally labile individuals show an excessive amount of increase in the curvature of the curved lines, while the converse is true for individuals who are constricted in their emotional responsiveness. Decreases in curvature occasionally are seen in individuals who are depressed or who have low frustration tolerance and rush through the difficult task of approximating the curves in a rapid, impulsive manner. Such an approach to the test results in decreased curvature. Similar findings occur in overtly hostile patients.

Byrd[6] has found that changes in curvature reflect emotional disturbance.

Children in need of psychotherapy have particular difficulty in reproducing curved stimulus figures.

Summary criteria: Any change in the curvature of a figure, manifest as: (a) *flattening:* reduction in the amplitude of a curve; (b) *increase* in the amplitude of a curve; (c) *spiking:* use of straight lines for upper and lower portions of a curve; (d) *irregularity:* incoordination in the line quality of a curve or curved line; (e) changes in total size of the curve(s).

14. *Change in Angulation*

This refers to change in the angle of intersection of parts of the designs or changes in angulation of the drawing from that which was present in the stimulus. Change in angulation occurs frequently in connection with design 6. In this design the two sinusoidal curves intersect each other so that the angle of intersection is obtuse on one side and acute on the other. A change in angulation, for example, would involve drawing these two designs so that they intersected at right angles or increasing the obtuseness of the angle of the intersection. We judge the drawing to show *increased angulation* when the acute angles are made more acute than in the original designs; similarly, we consider the change to be *decreased angulation* when the acute angles are made less acute in the reproduction than in the original. One further example may make this clear. In the case of design 2, the patient will sometimes arrange the columns of circles so that they appear to be at right angles to the horizontal plane. This represents a decrease in angulation since the original acute angles of the column from the horizontal plane are made less acute, in fact, are changed to right angles in the illustration given.

Our findings indicate a high correlation between the phenomena of changes in angulation and those of changes in curvature. Increased angulation indicates excessive reaction to emotional stimuli, while decreased angulation indicates the reverse. Evidence from the two factors just described is very helpful in determining the characteristic modes of response to external emotional traumata. This type of evidence is useful in assessing the probable effect, for example, of uncovering therapy or of unduly stimulating environmental situations.

Difficulty in reproducing angles is often a factor in syndromes associated with organic brain damage and with mental deficiency. Such individuals experience great difficulty in reproducing angles, often "dog-earring" them or "rounding" the angle.

Byrd's study[6] offers evidence that change in angulation is a factor capable of discriminating between adjusted and nonadjusted children.

Story[37] was able to confirm the hypothesis that alcoholics, in elaborating figure 2 of the RBGT, would attempt to reduce the emotional impact of the angulated columns of circles in this figure by changing the degree of their angulation.

Summary criterion: Any change of five degrees or more in the patient's reproduction of an angle constitutes this factor. Increased angulation refers to an increase in the acuteness of angles; decreased angulation refers to a decrease in the acuteness of angles.

Factors Relating to Distortion of the Gestalt

The various types of distortion which are described below are to be regarded as evidence of pathologic functioning. These types of responses are most characteristic of the psychotic population, but they are also found in other populations and they may occur as a consequence of an acute and intensive trauma resulting in transient disorganization of the personality and temporary loss of some ego controls. Nevertheless, the repetitive presence of one or more of these factors is to be regarded as prima facie evidence of a psychotic reaction even though the total personality structure of the patient may not be entirely similar to that of a psychotic individual. Even infrequent distortions are indicative of loss of ego control, temporary or otherwise, and therefore are of major significance in the interpretation of test records.

15. *Rotation*

This refers to a reproduction of the drawing in which there is a rotation of the major axis of the figure. This is to be distinguished from cases in which the patient rotates the stimulus card and then copies it accurately in that position, and also from cases in which the patient produces a "rotation" as a result of some shift in the drawing paper while engaged in copying a figure. This latter type of occurrence is not called rotation and, if present in a record, should be described by the examiner in some appropriate way so as to be able to distinguish it from rotation as we have defined it.

Rotation of the axis may be categorized as *mild, moderate,* or *severe.* The direction of the rotation may be characterized as *counterclockwise* or *clockwise.* Rotations of approximately 180 degrees are termed *reversals.*

Although rotation may occur in the records of all clinical groups, it is most frequently found in the records of individuals who are psychotic, have intracranial pathology, or are mentally defective. The mild type of rotation, 5 to 15 degrees, is indicative of depressive tendencies when the rotation is in a clockwise direction, and of antagonistic or oppositional trends when the rotation is counterclockwise. Specifically testing the hypothesis that mild counterclockwise rotations indicate oppositional tendencies, Story[37] provides evidence confirming this assertion. Rotations of 90 degrees in a counterclockwise direction suggest severe conflict with authority figures. Reversals are occasionally seen in negativistic individuals who may have collateral reading difficulties.

An important characteristic of the phenomenon of rotation concerns the degree of awareness by the patient of his rotational error. In general, awareness by the patient of his rotation is indicative of transitional difficulties in the perceptual area. Regressed schizophrenics and organic patients with severe psychopathology are usually unaware that their reproductions show rotation. Thus, when rotation occurs, it is well to test for degree of awareness during the testing the limits phase of the test.

Although severe rotation is relatively frequent among the schizophrenic group, approximately 30 per cent of schizophrenics, especially in the early stages of this disease, show little or no rotation. In such records, however, careful analysis will usually reveal other evidence of the psychotic process. In most instances when rotation does not appear in the records of schizophrenics, one may expect to find that the illness is of a bland or episodic variety. In interpreting severe rotation as evidence of a profound ego disturbance, it is important to consider other factors, such as the organization and changes in the size of the Gestalten. For example, if a record shows rigid sequence and all the figures are reduced in size, then the presence of the additional factor of severe rotation is indicative of a very severe ego disturbance in a person with compensatory controls. The interpretation follows from the attempts at extreme overcontrol of the patient (rigid sequence, reduction of size) which is nevertheless unsuccessful since rotation is also present. Such a record is indicative of much more severe pathology than that in which rotation occurs together with irregular sequence and impulsively or carelessly drawn reproductions. Persons with character disorders, for example, may produce records of the latter kind.

As indicated above, rotation is also present in the records of patients with organic brain damage. Hanvik and Anderson[19] found rotations of 30 degrees or more to be a significant characteristic of brain-damaged patients.

Summary criterion: Rotation refers to change in the orientation of the major axis of the figure. It does *not* refer to accurate reproductions when the stimulus or paper is rotated. Rotation may be characterized as: (a) *mild*, in which case the axis is rotated approximately 5 to 15 degrees; (b) *moderate*, in which case the axis is rotated approximately 15 to 80 degrees; and (c) *severe*, in which case the axis is rotated 80 to 180 degrees. The direction of rotation may be characterized as *counterclockwise* or *clockwise*.

16. *Retrogression*

This refers to the factor of substitution by the patient of a more primitive Gestalt for the Gestalt which the stimulus presents. Examples of retrogression are the use of loops instead of circles or well-formed curves, the persistent use of dashes instead of dots, and the use of dots for circles. The presence of retrogression must be judged by a comparative study of the evidence in relation to the patient's reproduction of more mature Gestalt forms. Since, in the normal development of the individual, some of the regressed signs may appear as a part of that early stage of maturation, *retrogression refers only to instances in which there is specific evidence that the individual has attained an all-over higher maturational level but shows more primitive Gestalt patterns in the instances under consideration.* (Of course, this criterion is particularly significant when judging retrogression in records of children's drawings.) It is debatable whether, in the case of retrogression, the individual has truly reverted to a form of behavior which is entirely that of a previous period in his development or whether he is simply showing only some of the characteristics of an earlier stage of his development. In any case, retrogression means that there is a loss in the effectiveness of the individual's ego functions, and such a loss is characteristic of a profound disturbance (acute or chronic) in the personality. It is always interesting to note the figures in which retrogression occurs, whether in the copy phase or elaboration phase of the procedure, and to develop some inferences regarding the nature of the conflict or trauma which has precipitated the regressive phenomona. Such inferences can be based, in the first place, on the symbolic meaning of the figure which produces the retrogressed material. In addition, the following suggestions may be helpful.

By the mental age of three the ability to reproduce a circular form has developed. At about the mental age of five the individual is capable of drawing an adequate square. The ability to draw a diamond form does not appear until the mental age of seven. Loops precede dashes developmentally, and dashes precede dots. However, the use of dashes, for example, as a replacement for dots, or loops as a replacement for circles, may be indicative of impulsivity, hostility, and a low frustration tolerance as well as of retrogression. Whether there is a profound ego disturbance resulting in retrogression or whether these other factors account for the destruction of the Gestalt form can be determined on the basis of the individual's test behavior as well as the level of maturity manifest in the other drawings in the test. Individuals characteristically impulsive and hostile will be consistent in their use of "retrogressed" forms.

Summary criterion: Retrogression is indicated by the substitution of more primitive for more mature Gestalten, provided other evidence for the distortions in the drawings cannot account for these phenomena.

17. *Simplification*

This factor is distinguishable from retrogression in that the reproduction of the Gestalt is inaccurate but is not a reversion to a more primitive form.

Rather, the Gestalt is replaced by a different form which logically may seem to be more complex but, from the point of view of the task, is more simple for the patient. An example of simplification in figure 7 (overlapping hexagons) is the reproduction of this design as two non-overlapping figures, although each of the figures may be reproduced accurately. Another example is the reproduction of figure A as an adjacent circle and square, both on the same axis.

Simplification represents an attempt by the patient to meet a situation which is too difficult for him by utilizing a less appropriate although still relevant response. The patient may be unwilling, as well as unable, to assert the effort and concentration necessary to draw the figure accurately, and he simplifies the figure so that he can deal with it more easily. Simplification by itself does not necessarily indicate the presence of an ego disturbance of psychotic proportions, although it is frequently associated with such a process and hence is included in this general category of test factors. It does represent, in any case, however, an inability to meet or deal effectively with the reality situation. It is found most frequently in cases in which marked feelings of impotence are present. Hence, one may expect to find it in those cases of brain damage in which the individual is aware of his severe limitation in functional capacity and is struggling, without effective solution, to meet the difficulty. In such cases the patient may verbalize his inability to produce a Gestalt or he may make repeated efforts to improve on his inadequate performance. Simplification is more serious and more likely to be indicative of a psychotic process when the patient, even under questioning, is unable to perceive the difference which exists between his reproduction and the original stimulus.

It should be noted, however, that simplification may also indicate low frustration tolerance, negativism, or overt hostility and occurs when the patient is grudgingly participating in the examination. Such an approach to the test situation is frequently characteristic of the passive-aggressive individual. Test behavior and evidence from other aspects of the test drawings are useful in differentiating simplification as a resultant of such factors from that associated with more severe psychopathology.

Summary criterion: Simplification refers to the replacement of a Gestalt figure with a different and simplified figure (or figures), which is *not*, however, more primitive than the original.

18. *Fragmentation*

This refers to the destruction of the original Gestalt and the reproduction of only a part of it or of all of it as separate parts. It is manifested most frequently in incomplete drawings, but occasionally it is shown in drawings in which the parts of an integral whole are dissociated. It is to be distinguished from simplification in that there is a basic destruction of the Gestalt even though all of the separate elements may be present.

This phenomenon is associated with severe psychotic disturbances and seems to represent a loss in both the abstraction and organizational capacities. It is also associated with some types of cases involving brain damage. It represents a loss in ability to synthesize perceptual stimuli, or a loss in ability to synthesize the motoric behavior with the perceptual response.

Since fragmentation appears to involve losses in the capacity for abstracting and synthesizing experience, its presence in cases of severe psychosis, frontal brain damage, and the like is easily understood. It will also become evident, upon reflection, why it may be found in cases of hysterical amnesia and in cases with acute, intense anxiety.

Summary criterion: Reproduction of a Gestalt figure which involves breaking it up into parts or reproduction of an incomplete figure.

19. *Overlapping Difficulty*

This refers to difficulty in drawing designs which overlap, especially figures 4, 6, and 7. Overlapping is scored when there is any evidence of difficulty in reproducing the portions of the figure which overlap. The patient may manifest this difficulty by such phenomena as the following: failure to reproduce portions of the figure which overlap, simplification of either figure at the point of overlap, sketching or redrawing of the overlapping portions, distortion of the figure at the point of overlap. Very often this factor is associated with *simplification* and *fragmentation,* and it may be that it is not a separate factor at all, although our present evidence suggests that it may be present without the occurence of the other factors and that somewhat different phenomena are involved. Overlapping difficulty occurs most frequently in cases of organic brain damage which involve the occipital-parietal regions. These brain areas apparently serve as the repository for visual-motor organization. Consequently, any disturbance in these areas will most likely result in a disruption of these functions.

Summary criterion: This factor is scored when the patient's reproductions of overlapping figures manifest such difficulties as: failure to reproduce portions of the figure which overlap, simplification of either figure at the point of overlap, sketching or redrawing of the overlapping portions, distortion of the figure at the point of overlap.

20. *Elaboration or Doodling*

There is some doubt that this factor belongs among those we have placed in the category of items which we have called distortion of the Gestalt. The term is probably self-explanatory, and refers to the patient's elaborating or doodling over the original Gestalt form, changing its general appearance markedly in many instances. Its presence in a test protocol indicates a severe disturbance of the associative functions as well as impairment in ability to concentrate. It is found most frequently in psychotic individuals, particularly among those with manic tendencies. It also occurs frequently in other psychopathologies in which agitation and disturbances in cognitive control are present. Neurotics with intense anxiety also show this phenomenon. The attempt by the patient to elaborate the design by adding additional lines or curves not present in the original stimulus is indicative of a severe disturbance in ego functioning, even though in some instances the disturbance may be temporary. Thus, the significance of this factor for a particular patient can be fully evaluated only in the light of other evidence.

Summary criterion: This factor is scored if the patient adds to the original Gestalt form by doodling or elaborating and thus markedly changing its appearance.

21. *Perseveration (A)*

This factor (A) refers to the persistent or continued use in a subsequent drawing of features of a preceding stimulus figure. For example, the patient may replace the circles in figure 2 with dots, due to perseveration of the dot-performing behavior required in figure 1. In the same way, a patient may reproduce figure 3 using circles instead of dots because he is perseverating on the basis of the circles in figure 2.

Perseveration of this type is indicative of decreased ego control and of impairment in reality testing. It is most characteristic of those nosologic groups in which a rather profound disturbance has occurred or in which there has been an arrest in development. It represents an inability to attend completely to a new stimulus due to a "lag" effect of a previous stimulus. Persons with poor ego cathexis may display such behavior. This factor consequently occurs frequently among psychotics and mental defectives. It is also occasionally found in the records of individuals with intracranial pathology, but is not as frequent as is factor 22 below.

Summary criterion: Substitution, inappropriately, of features of a preceding stimulus, such as replacing the circles of figure 2 with the dots of figure 1, constitute this factor.

22. *Perseveration (B)*

This factor (B) refers to test behavior in which the patient continues the Gestalt beyond the limits called for by the stimulus. In other words, he does not stop when the Gestalt is reproduced accurately, but continues to repeat part or all of the stimulus. Thus, in figure 1, he may continue to draw dots until he reaches the edge of the page, or in figure 2, he may do the same kind of thing with the columns of circles. In extreme instances of this kind of perseveration, the Gestalt will be continued until the edge of the paper is reached and the drawing may even be continued on the desk or table. Perseveration B occurs most frequently on figures 1, 2, and 5.

The example of perseveration B which occurs when the patient repeats the entire stimulus figure is relatively rare. This kind of perseveration, moreover, must be distinguished from instances in which the patient tries to correct a drawing by making another attempt at it. Usually, observation of the patient's test behavior or questioning of the patient will enable the examiner to make the differentiation.

Perseveration B seems to reflect extreme rigidity in personality as well as some loss of the critical function. It also reflects the patient's inability to shift from a set developed during the reproduction of a figure to a new set required when he reaches the end of the stimulus. This phenomenon is fairly frequent in severely compulsive individuals and occurs most frequently in cases of organic brain damage. When it appears in organic individuals, it seems to represent a "short-circuiting" of the associative functions of the brain. It points up the rigidity of the so-called organic syndrome.

Summary criterion: Inappropriately continuing the Gestalt, during reproduction, beyond the limits called for by the stimulus. It is not scored in figure 1 unless the patient produces 14 or more dots. In figure 2, it is not scored unless the patient produces 13 or more rows of circles.

Movement and Drawing Factors

23. *Movement Determinants*

There are three basic characteristics of movement determinants. (a) Although most patients use both clockwise and counterclockwise directions of movement, to some extent, the characteristic direction of movement in a right-handed person is in a counterclockwise orientation. Left-handed individuals, somewhat more frequently, use clockwise movements. When the characteristic direction of movement is contrary to that expected, some form of psychopathology should be suspected. In general, the general direction of movement is contrary to expectation in persons with strong oppositional, especially passive-oppositional, tendencies. Clinical data also suggests that persons showing such characteristics overemphasize in their defensive hierarchy such mechanisms as denial, isolation, and reversal.

There are other features of the direction of movement about which we may offer only tentative suggestions. (b) One of these is the characteristic tendency to draw vertical lines from the bottom up rather than from the top down. This tendency has been found to be frequently associated with neurotic fear of authority figures. (c) When the characteristic movement is from the outside of the design to the internal part of the design, narcissistic trends and general egocentricity of personality is suggested.[28] The latter tendency is probably associated with centripetal factors in the personality, on the one hand, and with centripetal M on the Rorschach. Unfortunately, evidence is lacking concerning the effect of original-handedness and related questions upon the characteristic direction of movement.

Summary criteria: (a) Deviation from the expected direction of movement constitutes one aspect of this factor. Such movement is generally counterclockwise in right-handed people and clockwise in left-handed people. (b) Deviation in the drawing of vertical lines is another movement determinant. The characteristic direction used in drawing such lines is from the top down. (c) The third aspect of movement determinants is noted in those individuals who show a tendency to make their characteristic movements from the outside to the internal portion of the Gestalten.

24. *Consistency in the Direction of Movement*

This factor is related to the fact that most individuals characteristically utilize one or another of the basic movement orientations. When a patient shows discrepancies between his characteristic movement orientation on some designs with his movement orientation on another design, the phenomenon is referred to as *inconsistency in the direction of movement.* Such inconsistencies are related to psychic blocking, oftentimes associated with the symbolic meaning of the stimulus, and are usually indicative of ongoing attempts by the patient to act out strongly conflictual trends in his personality. Evidence of this kind has some favorable connotations, since the patient is still actively striving to work out a solution to his difficulties. When it occurs, we can infer that there is sufficient ego strength to indicate either some favorable aspects in the prognosis or that the condition is one that is still in an acute or prodromal stage.

Summary criterion: A sudden change by the patient from his characteristic direction of movement during his reproduction of a design or the part of a design constitutes this factor.

25. *Line Quality*

This refers to the characteristic kinds of pencil strokes used by the patient in completing the drawing task. The first point to be noticed is whether or not the patient's line quality is consistent throughout all of his drawings. When consistency is present, it may be inferred that the individual's adjustment, be it good or bad, is relatively stable. When inconsistencies occur, for example, sudden increases or decreases in the intensity of the line quality, it may be inferred that some conflict area has been triggered by the symbolic value of the particular stimulus figure. Specific information regarding this conflict may often be obtained in the association phase of the test administration. When inconsistencies in line quality occur throughout all of the nine Gestalt figures, it may be inferred that the individual's adjustment and defenses are highly unstable or in a state of current fluctuation. The following kinds of line quality have been differentiated:

(a) *Heavy lines.* When these are present with relatively no deviation and tend to taper off toward the end of a pencil stroke, they are most generally indicative of overtly hostile impulses. This factor most often occurs in conjunction with increased size of figures, irregular sequence, and excessive use of space. It is occasionally accompanied by collision tendencies in severely disturbed individuals.

(b) *Heavy lines accompanied by incoordination.* This type of response usually indicates unsuccessful and compensatory attempts at control associated with residual tension or anxiety. It is, therefore, frequently found in the test protocols of individuals with organic brain damage as well as in those with acute anxiety over unresolved drives.

(c) *Faint lines.* This phenomenon, resulting from inadequate pencil pressure, is frequently associated with timidity and anxiety in individuals who tend to use withdrawal as a primary defense. Such individuals are often unable to express their hostile impulses in appropriately aggressive behavior.

(d) *Poor coordination.* This factor is present when the lines which make up the patient's drawings are irregular rather than smooth-flowing. This irregularity may be fine, with a tremulousness seldom exceeding one thirty-second of an inch, or coarse, with the tremor having an amplitude in excess of one-sixteenth of an inch. Poor coordination is frequently present in the test records of patients manifesting overt tension and anxiety as well as in cases of organic brain damage. When the incoordination is of the coarse variety, anxiety may be intense, or there may be neurologic damage of a subcortical or spinal nature.

(e) *Sketching.* This refers to the resketching and retouching of a simple line. It must be distinguished from the type of art sketching which results in a reproduction which is well-conceived and adequately completed. This sketching consists of many abortive line movements; the final product is inferior in quality and occasionally results in an inaccurate reproduction of the Gestalt. Sketching indicates anxiety as well as uncertainty and feelings of insecurity on the part of the patient.

Summary criteria: The kinds of pencil lines utilized by patients in their reproduction of the Gestalten constitute this factor. The quality of the lines may be consistent throughout the drawings or inconsistent. (a) Heavy lines are drawn with substantial pencil pressure and tend to taper off at the end of the pencil stroke. (b) Heavy lines accompanied by incoordination are also drawn with pressure, but are not smooth and free-flowing; they tend to be irregular and tremulous. (c) Faint lines are drawn with inadequate pencil pressure and are far lighter than lines drawn with usual pressure. They represent the other end of the continuum from heavy lines. (d) Poor co-ordination is identified by irregularity and tremulousness in line quality. Fine irregularity has an amplitude that does not exceed one thirty-second of an inch; coarse irregularity has an amplitude in excess of one-sixteenth of an inch. (e) Sketching consists of repetitive attempts at the completion of a straight line or curve, resulting in an inadequate or inaccurate reproduction of the Gestalt.

Table 1 presents a summary of the test factors discussed above.

TABLE I. *Summary Criteria of Test Factors*

Factor	Scoring Criteria	Illustrations*
1. Sequence		
a. overly methodical	No deviation from a fixed, rigid organization.	
b. methodical	No more than two deviations.	30, 96
c. irregular	More than two deviations, but the patient's plan is still determinable.	115, 126
d. confused or symbolic	A sequence with no apparent logic. A sequence with symbolic value to the patient.	
2. Position of the First Drawing	Any placement of figure A other than the following is atypical: (1) in a rectangular area one inch from the left margin and top of the page extending to one inch from the right margin and then down two inches; (2) the upper left-hand corner of the page.	103, 117
3. Use of Space I		
a. excessive	Space between 2 drawings is more than $\frac{1}{2}$ of the corresponding axis of either figure.	129
b. constricted	Space between 2 drawings is less than $\frac{1}{4}$ of the corresponding axis of either figure.	105, 108
c. normal	Less space than a but more than b.	96
Use of Space II		
a. excessive	Factor 3a present in a record two or more times.	30
b. constricted	Factor 3b present in a record two or more times.	105, 133
4. Collision	A figure actually running into one or more other figures.	126, 130
a. collision tendency	Placement of a figure within $\frac{1}{4}$ inch of another figure.	100, 126
5. Use of Margin	Placing 7 or more figures within $\frac{1}{4}$ inch of the margin.	96
6. Shift in the Position of the Paper	Rotation of the paper, on its initial presentation, at least or more than 90 degrees.	

*Pages on which examples of these factors are discussed.

TABLE I. *Summary Criteria of Test Factors—Continued.*

Factor	Scoring Criteria	Illustrations
7. Shift in the Position of the Stimulus Cards	Turning the stimulus card 90 or more degrees from its position on initial presentation.	
8. Over-all Increase or Decrease in Size of the Figures	An increase or decrease of the drawing in at least one axis by more than $\frac{1}{4}$ of the corresponding axis of the stimulus qualifies as a change in size. Over-all increase or decrease is scored if changes occur in five or more drawings.	34, 157
9. Progressive Increase or Decrease in Size	Increased or decreased size, by any amount, sequentially in six drawings.	30
10. Isolated Increase or Decrease in Size (Dilation or Cohesion)	An increase or decrease, in size of a figure or part of a figure, of at least $\frac{1}{4}$ of the corresponding axis in the stimulus, by $\frac{1}{4}$ more or less of the dimensions used in the rest of the figure, or by $\frac{1}{4}$ more or less of the dimensions used in the preceding or subsequent drawing.	105, 155
11. Closure Difficulty	Gaps, overworking, erasures, increased pressure at points where parts of the design join one another.	33, 99
12. Crossing Difficulty	Redrawing, sketching, erasures, increase of pressure at the point of line crossings in any figure.	101, 110
13. Curvature Difficulty	Any changes in the curves in a figure, such as increased amplitude, spiking, flattening, irregularity, changes in size.	105, 153
14. Change in Angulation	Any change of more than 5 degrees in the reproduction of an angle.	
a. increased	Increased acuity.	
b. decreased	Decreased acuity.	34, 105
15. Rotation	Rotation of the major axis of a figure.	
a. mild	5 to 15 degrees.	99, 117
b. moderate	15 to 80 degrees.	105, 136
c. severe	80 to 180 degrees.	
16. Retrogression	Substitution of more primitive forms for more mature forms, provided that evidence of the patient's capability of producing mature forms is otherwise present.	117, 129
17. Simplification	Replacement of parts of a Gestalt with a different and simplified form which is not more primitive from a maturational point of view.	35, 106
18. Fragmentation	Reproduction of a figure by breaking it into parts or reproducing an incomplete figure.	110, 133

TABLE I. *Summary Criteria of Test Factors—Continued.*

Factors	Scoring Criteria	Illustrations
19. Overlapping Difficulty	Difficulty with overlapping figures, manifest by failure to reproduce portions of the figure which overlap: simplification of either figure at the point of overlap, sketching or redrawing of the overlapping portions, distortion of the figure at the point of overlap.	112, 130
20. Elaboration or Doodling	Adding to the original Gestalt by elaboration or doodling.	
21. Perseveration A	Substitution, inappropriately, of features of a preceding stimulus: replacing the circles of figure 2 with the dots of figure 1; replacing the dots of figure 3 and 5 with the circles of figure 2.	128
22. Perseveration B	Continuing, inappropriately, the Gestalt beyond the limits called for by the stimulus. For figure 1, 14 or more dots must be present; for figure 2, 13 or more rows of circles.	106, 128
23. Movement Determinants	Atypical movement as follows: clockwise movement in a right-handed person, counterclockwise movement in a left-handed person, vertical lines drawn from the bottom up, movement from the outside to the inside of a Gestalt.	
24. Inconsistancy in the Direction of Movement	A sudden change from the characteristic direction of movement.	101
25. Line Quality		
a. heavy lines	Dark in color, drawn with heavy pressure which can be detected by running the finger over the back of the paper and feeling the resulting ridge; a tendency to taper off at the end of the pencil stroke.	30, 109
b. heavy lines with incoordination	The factors in 25a above, with irregularity and tremulousness.	35
c. faint lines	Lines are light, drawn with little pencil pressure.	130
d. poor coordination, fine	Irregularity of lines with an amplitude not exceeding $\frac{1}{32}$ of an inch.	129, 152
poor coordination, coarse	Irregularity of lines, amplitude exceeding $\frac{1}{16}$ of an inch.	
e. sketching	Repetitive attempts at completion of a line resulting in an inadequate reproduction.	110

It may be of interest to report some recent findings with respect to inter-judge reliability for these test factors. Previous research has already yielded significant correlations between the various test factors, as scored by various research workers, and personality factors (refs. 6, 7, and 37, for example). However, insufficient data are available on the interjudge reliability of each of the several test factors.

A recent study conducted by one of the present authors and now being prepared for publication indicates that interjudge reliability for 19 of the factors, taken together, is quite good. Giving equal weight to each of the test factors, and assigning a range of scores from 1 to 10 on the basis of the criteria defined above, a Pearson correlation coefficient of .91 was obtained for the total test scores obtained by two graduate students on a population of 20 hospitalized schizophrenics. This finding is all the more significant in view of the fact that neither of these scorers had had any previous experience with this scoring scheme.* Some of the findings on specific test factors may be of interest. The following Pearson r's were obtained: sequence: .80; position of the first figure: .90; closure difficulty: .69; curvature change: .51; angulation: .73; rotation: .79; retrogression: .74; fragmentation: .70; simplification: .71; perseveration: .96. Although it may be expected that the findings will vary with other populations, probably being higher for a more heterogeneous population, the data indicate that the reliability is sufficiently high to warrant continued use and further research.

---

*The authors are indebted to Robert Gunn and Mary Kemme for their contribution to this study.

VI

Principles of Inferential and Configurational Analysis

In this chapter we shall discuss two types of separate but complementary analyses of the RBGT. We shall deal with problems of inferential analysis first and then discuss the findings and interpretation of configurational analysis. The latter type of analysis lends itself more easily to statistical treatment since it implies that different types of configurations of signs or factors mean different kinds of things and the differences between or among various sets of configurations may be subjected to tests of statistical significance. All that is needed are clear specifications of the various configurations and clear statements of criteria of the differing phenomena which each configuration supposedly predicts. The former type of analysis may involve a whole series of sequential inferences, which may or may not be precisely replicable in different cases and therefore involves a more complicated validation problem.

Inferential Analysis

Inferential analysis depends, in the first instance, on the presence of discrete phenomena which already have a substantial body of data for validation purposes. However, this type of analysis goes beyond the simple statement of a correlational relationship between each phenomenon and each "trait." It assumes, on the contrary, that the successive productions of a given sequence of events are uniquely determined by the interaction of multidetermined events over a span of time so that the final product on the test represents the idiosyncratic resultant of the *given constellation of events operating over time.* Moreover, it involves the postulation of not one but several alternate hypotheses during the process of developing inferences, until the analysis of sequential findings tends to confirm one or several of these hypotheses and simultaneously reject others. To illustrate, in a general way, what we mean by these latter two phases in sequential inference we may refer once again, as we did in Chapter III, to the problem of passivity. Supposing our test results indicate that, as one of the plausible hypotheses, the patient in question shows passivity. We may have come to this inference on the basis of such evidence as: light line drawings, reduction of the Gestalten in the vertical plane, increased size of the figures involving curved lines, and difficulty with intersecting figures. Assuming that passivity is indeed present, we are now confronted with such questions as: "Is the passivity a reaction formation to pronounced aggressive drives?" or "Is the passivity part of a feminine orientation on the part of the patient?" or "Is the passivity part of a general withdrawal of cathexes or of some other type of withdrawal?" At this point we have to examine the test data before and especially after those points at which the passive phenomena appeared. We may then find that the patient responds only to certain figures by passive withdrawal, that during the elaboration phase of the test, when he is offered greater freedom, passive characteristics do not occur, and that during the association phase he offers a number of marked but covert responses (symbolic) of aggression, like "hitting," "tearing," "cutting," and "disintegrating." In the light of the total response repertoire, and particularly in the light of successive sequences during which passivity occurs or fails to occur, we may be led to some final inference concerning the meaning, intensity, and etiology of the phenomenon of passivity.

There are many ways in which to start the process of inferential analysis. One might begin with the first figure on the test, "speculate" concerning the specific features of the reproduction on this figure (or, more precisely, list the separate hypotheses which all of the features of the reproduction might suggest), and then move on in sequence to each of the subsequent figures, following this, in turn, with a similar type of analysis of the material from the elaboration and association phases. However, this type of procedure fails to take into account the general stylistic qualities of the total set of drawings, and we believe it is generally desirable to begin with this feature of the test. The major argument for this proposal is that the general style of the patient, as revealed in the over-all organization and arrangement of the drawings on the page (and the repetition or modification of this style in the various phases of the test) reveals the most general and pervasive qualities of the patient's personality at the time of the test, and thereby offers some important and convenient parameters within which to organize the several separate and successive inferences from each of the drawings.[28] To contrast one aspect of "style" in two patients in order to make this point more meaningful, suppose we had the records of two adult patients, one of which showed a crowding of the nine figures within the confines of the upper one-third of a single page, while the other showed a "distribution" of the figures over three pages. We could infer from the first patient's record a reaction of extreme withdrawal, perhaps suspiciousness as well as marked anxiety, in the face of a relatively nonthreatening test situation. We could, similarly, infer from the other record, the reaction of an extratensive individual, perhaps manic in quality, perhaps egocentric and the like, with relatively little overt anxiety or suspiciousness. Having offered such types of general hypotheses about each patient, we could then go on to test them, add to them, or modify them in the light of the several features of each of the separate drawings.

We shall begin, then, with features concerning the general style of the patient's drawings. The following suggestions may be applied separately to the drawings obtained from each phase of the test (or each method). When these several and separate analyses have been made from the data obtained in each phase, they may then be integrated into the most parsimonious set of explanations and predictions for the entire set of drawings.

The first question which confronts us is how much *space* the patient used for all of the drawings. Was it excessive, constricted, or normal (in terms of the criteria listed in Chapter V)? The amount of space used tells us something concerning the patient's self-percept vis-a-vis the rest of the world. Further, the ways in which he uses space as he moves through the total test tells us how adaptable he is in respect to this general orientation he has with regard to his world. It is highly useful in analyzing this portion of the data to try to emphathize with the patient's actual performance so that, in addition to the hypotheses we have offered in Chapter V concerning the use of space, we can derive tentative, alternative hypotheses concerning the specific ways in which this particular patient used space as he proceeded through the successive portions of the test.

Next, having extricated all of the possible inferences we can from the patient's use of space, we may turn our attention to the problem of *sequence*. Here, we start again with the criteria listed in the previous chapter, noting all of the hypotheses which the data suggest concerning sequence. These are noted, first, without regard to whether or not they appear to be in conflict with the hypotheses derived from the analysis of space. Moreover, any idiosyncratic features of the sequence such as, for example, a generally orderly sequence with an outstanding exception, say, on figure 6 (the sinusoidal curves) in which a marked change in sequence appears, followed by an orderly sequence for the remaining figures, is noted and hypotheses developed. One would want to consider the possible difficulties which figure 6 might impose upon this or any patient, and the possible reaction to the previous figure in the light of what is known about these figures (see later discussion in this chapter). Having formed these two general sets of hypotheses, from the use of space and from sequence, it would be well, next, to attempt to reconcile them, being sure not to discard any hypothesis which cannot clearly be rejected. In this process, hypotheses of a higher, more integrated order might appear, or additional, alternative hypotheses, not deducible alone from either space or sequence, might be formed.

The next step in the general analysis of style concerns the *placement of the first figure*. Here again, as with the problem of the use of space, the patient's initial stylistic adaptation to his life space can be inferred (see Chapter V). Does he, for example, place his first figure (i.e., himself) in the middle of the page, suggesting a highly egocentric orientation with respect to the world, or does he squeeze the first figure into the upper, left-hand corner of the page, suggesting extreme withdrawal and fearfulness? Of course, the nature of the reproduction of the first figure (figure A) will enter into the speculative hypotheses which may be offered, but we shall leave until later the discussion of the separate figures. Once again, having made whatever hypotheses seem plausible on the basis of this stylistic feature, we attempt to integrate these with the previous hypotheses which have been derived.

Next, we note whether any collision or near collision phenomena are present. Such data are indicative of loss of anticipatory controls and are most frequently associated with either marked anxiety (basic or transitional) or with intracranial damage and possible loss in psychological control or in motor control. In either case, there is an impairment of ego functions, and we carefully note the adaptation made during and following the figures on which collision tendencies occur. For instance, collision tendencies involving curved figures differ from those involving straight-line figures; the former are more likely to be associated with difficulty in expressing aggressive drives; the latter are more likely to be associated with passive drives. As another example, collision involving more complex figures, like 7 and 8, but not simple figures like 3 and 4, are more likely to relate to loss in cognitive rather than emotional factors. We also examine the drawings to determine whether the patient is aware of or attempts to correct his collision phenomena. Such behavior indicates at least marginal awareness of the perceptual-motoric problem and, when corrected placement occurs after collision, is indicative of modifiability of response pattern—a highly useful finding in terms of therapeutic management and prognosis.

Another general stylistic feature refers to the use of the margin. We have already noted the most probable hypotheses associated with this phenomenon (Chapter V). We can offer a number of hypotheses based on the general use of the margin and others based on the use of the margin for some of the individual figures alone. (See Chapter X, for example.) If, by this point in our analysis of a particular record, consistent hypotheses have been derived from the several sources of data concerning general style, we can be reasonably certain that these are strong hypotheses. Further indication of their strength may be derived from subsequent analyses of the separate figures, and then again from analysis of the data obtained during the elaboration phase of the test.

One other general source of hypotheses derived from stylistic features is that of rotation of the test paper and the test cards. Hypotheses related to egocentricity and/or rigidity are based on rotations of 90 degrees to about 180 degrees, while those related to oppositional qualities are based on rotation of 180 degrees or more.

All of the inferences derived thus far are based upon the overt behavior shown by the patient during the test and in his responses. To the extent that the behavior has obvious meaning to the patient, as, for example, when he rotates the cards despite the structuring of the test in opposition to such placement, or when he places his first figure in the center of the page, we can assume that the phenomena in question are at the conscious or preconscious level. To the extent that the behavior has only latent meaning, such as, for example, when the sequence is changed because a particular figure has some symbolic threat for the patient, we can assume that unconscious factors are operating. Not only can we therefore make a rough categorization of the level of meaning of the behavior to the patient (from conscious to unconscious), but by virtue of our general knowledge of psychopathology and the operation of defenses, we can begin to infer some specific types of dynamics (nature and severity of conflict) for the patient. Such dynamic inferences, especially as they are reinforced or confirmed in the light of evidence associated with the distortions on the several figures and with data from the elaborations and associations, are powerful tools for predicting the nature and significance of unconscious processes for the patient. When these are integrated with the overt behavior of the patient they enable us to extend our clinical analysis to cover a wider variety of contingencies than when they are limited to only one source of data (see Chapter III).

Now we shall turn our attention to the separate Gestalt figures, commenting simultaneously on the other test factors as they are likely to emerge on these figures.

Figure A has several features to commend it as the initial figure in the test presentation. In the first place it is a relatively simple figure, requiring only a mental maturity corresponding roughly to about seven to eight years for its successful reproduction. It is therefore useful to compare relative success on this figure with performance on the other simple and on the other more complex figures (like figures 1, 2, 3, 4, on the one hand, and figures 6, 7, and 8 on the other). It can usually be assumed, for example, that consistently greater difficulty on the simple figures in comparison with the more difficult ones is due to intrapsychic difficulties rather than maturational problems.

Another feature concerning figure A is that it consists of two well-structured, closed, simple and *tangential* figures. The tangential aspect makes the figure particularly useful in detecting difficulties in interpersonal cathexes (joining and closure factors). Still another feature is the presence of two figures which have well-nigh universal symbolic meanings: the circle represents the female object and the square represents the male object. (It is, of course, important to test the applicability of these symbolic meanings for a particular patient. The patient's responses during the association phase of the test furnish one basis for such verification.) It is possible to infer that relative increases in size of one figure as compared with the other refer to problems in the patient's self-percept. Thus, for example, a patient who reproduces the square as greatly enlarged in proportion to the circle can be assumed to be attempting unconsciously to identify with a male role; the relative discrepancy in size is therefore indicative of difficulty in this identification for, otherwise, both figures would receive equal emphasis. This type of hypothesis can be checked against the elaborations and the associations in the other two phases of the basic method of administration. Patients who wish unconsciously to see themselves as more masculine will be likely to exaggerate the square during the elaboration by some such method as placing the circle within the square or by producing a number of squares around the circle as a pivot.

Another feature of figure A is that it consists of a curved and a straight-line figure. From clinical and experimental evidence we know that difficulty in expressing aggressive drives is associated with difficulty in reproducing curved figures whereas corresponding difficulty with passivity is associated with straight-line figures.* We have already commented on the problem of placement of the first figure. We can also add that, since this is the first figure in the test, whatever transient factors are associated with initial adaptation to the test situation are likely to be projected into some aspect of the performance on this figure. Hence, careful examination of all of the features in the reproduction of this figure is recommended. Comparison with the subsequent figures may make it possible to deduce which features are associated with problems in initial adaptation and which are more probably characterologic in nature.

Figure 1 consists of 12 equidistant dots. Because it is an unstructured figure (i.e., it has no clearly delineated boundary), it presents difficulties to some patients. Patients with organic problems find this figure more difficult than its inherent structure justifies (because of figure-ground perceptual

---

*See Breen, H.: "The differential diagnostic technique as a measure of hostility." Unpublished doctoral dissertation, University of Western Ontario, 1953; and North, S.: "The diagnostic efficiency of a drawing technique." Unpublished doctoral dissertation, University of Western Ontario, 1953.

problems associated with organic deficit). Patients with intense, diffuse anxiety also find the figure difficult for similar reasons. Patients with severe aspiration problems have difficulty in leaving this figure, as simple as it is; they spend a great deal of energy in filling in the dots or in emphasizing the circularity of the dots. To some patients with traumatic anxiety the dots are suggestive of bullets or pellets coming directly at them and, as a consequence, they may produce a very wavy line of dots. Some schizophrenic patients with high ideational and paranoid qualities elaborate the dots and may "extend" them into birds or symbolic figures or "doodles" (some anxious neurotics do the same thing). And, finally, a word may be said concerning obsessive-compulsive patients who spend an inordinate amount of time completing this simple figure because of their perfectionistic needs and frequently count and recount the number of dots.

The relative placements of figures A and 1 also deserve some comment. It is interesting to note the directional orientation which the patient takes after completing figure A. Does he move to the right, or does he move to a position directly below figure A in beginning figure 1? Preferred direction of movement is a stylistic feature which we have already commented on in the preceding chapter. Preferred movements in the lateral or horizontal plane, for example, are likely to be associated with unresolved needs for interpersonal cathexes, while movements in the vertical plane are related to difficulties in dealing with authority figures. Some patients, moreover, draw the line of dots in such a way that it represents an arc (sometimes barely discernible) with themselves as the pivot—indicative of an egocentric or, possibly, narcissistic orientation. Others draw the line of dots with a slight clockwise rotation, which is indicative of depressive trends. These and other general characteristics of the drawing of this figure are worth noting for the rich harvest of hypotheses which they may offer.

Again, we wish to emphasize that the contrast in performance and in general behavior which may be noted for the first two figures—or the consistency which is evident—is important for still other hypotheses which may be derived. Contrast may occur in size, in spacing, in directional orientation, in relative amount of time and energy expended in completing the task, and the like. One may lose sight of the sequential production of such phenomena if specific attention is not directed to this phase of the analysis, and, as a consequence of this, only discrete hypotheses which can be summated in a score of deviations or distortions remain.

Turning now to figure 2, we note that it consists of 10 angulated columns of circles. Because there is a shift from the dots of figure 1 to the circles of figure 2, we wish to attend particularly to the occurrence of perseveration which may first be manifest on figure 2 (although another type of perseveration may occur on figure 1). Some patients reproduce figure 2 with dots instead of circles, perseverating the dots of figure 1. This phenomenon is most characteristic of patients with severe ego impairment, such as psychotics, but it may occur when transient anxiety is very intense. The open character of this figure, like that of figure 1, since there is no clear indication of the boundary, is threatening to some patients. Organics and those with severe problems in interpersonal relationships sometimes have difficulty with this figure. When the figure is elongated in the lateral plane but the number of columns of circles is correct, we can infer that the problem is likely to be one of difficult interpersonal relations. When perservation of the dots of figure 1, or perseveration of the columns of circles is present, some organic hypothesis is more likely. Another feature of importance on this figure is any change in the angulation of the columns of circles. In general, reduction in the acuteness of the angulation corresponds to reduction in the affectivity of the patient, while increase in acuteness corresponds to increase in affectivity. Sometimes, the patient has difficulty in perceiving or in executing the angulation feature, as, for example, when he reproduces the columns as perpendicular to the base of the paper but rotates the whole figure in a counterclockwise manner to achieve some semblance of angulation. This kind of difficulty is associated with the feelings of impotence experienced by some organics; occasionally it may be present in the production of psychopaths. Still another phenomenon is the tendency to produce a figure with shifts in the angulation of the columns so that those at the left are produced with a relatively correct angulation but, as the other columns are drawn, the position of the columns tends to become more and more reversed, so that the whole figure describes an arc with the patient at the center or point of origin. As on figure 1, this phenomenon is indicative of egocentrism or narcissism. Some patients manifest a progressive and regressive shift in the angulation of the successive columns, an indication of compensatory attempts to maintain interpersonal cathexes. Some patients draw the figure with a clockwise orientation or rotation, an indication of depressive trends. If depressive features in the personality result in clockwise rotation, this feature is usually present in all three of the first three figures and the hypothesis is thus strongly supported. Moreover, other test features may be associated with the depression, such as light pressure in line movement and difficulty in completing any of the tasks. This combination of characteristics is usually associated with depression in a highly dependent and passive personality. When strong masochistic features are present, line pressure tends to be heavy. Another feature associated with masochism is the placement of dots within each of the circles. We have noted only some of the most important characteristics associated with the drawing of this figure. Many other such characteristics are present and correlated hypotheses may be deduced.

Figure 3, the arrowhead constructed of dots, is another open figure. Some patients who have managed to maintain some degree of control with the previous open figures finally begin to break down on this figure. (Organics usually show their ego impairment before they have reached this figure.) For other patients the aggressive qualities of this figure, or its symoblic meaning to them, is threatening. For such patients we may expect that some compensatory effort will be made to reduce the apparent threat. This may be done by compressing the figure, thus destroying its essential Gestalt, or by reducing the angularity of the angles in the figure. Another fairly frequent characteristic of the reproduction of this figure in the case of regressed patients is a simplification of the figure (by reducing the number of dots or by reducing the number of component parts). Depressive trends are also frequently manifest on this figure in the form of rotational difficulties of a minor degree. Patients with strong anal fixations tend to be overly careful with this figure, counting the dots again and again, but sometimes losing the general Gestalt in the process because of their overconcern with minutia. The specific associative meanings of this figure for the patient can frequently be easily inferred from the material in the elaboration and association phases of the test.

Figure 4, like figure A, presents two symbols which frequently are associated with sexual identification, the open square representing the male object and the curved figure representing the female object. It therefore has some of the same values as figure A. Confirmation of hypotheses dealing with identification can frequently be obtained by a comparison of the distortions on these two figures. Since figure 4 is more difficult than figure A, some problems usually emerge on this figure that have not been noted on figure A. The relative size of the curved portion of the figure in relation to the open square is particularly important in this respect. The tendency to flatten the curve or the tendency to produce an extra or excessive loop at the end of the curve is also important; the former is associated with emotional "flattening," the latter with impulsivity and poor emotional control. Some patients have difficulty with the vertical sides of the open square, indicative of difficulty in authority relationships. This difficulty may be shown in a number of ways, such as sketching on the vertical sides, successive attempts to increase or extend these sides, or an increase in the dimensions of these sides. Other patients show fairly marked closure problems on this figure. Still others fragment the figure or separate the two components. The latter is associated with the severe ego impairment occurring in regressive states and in problems associated with organicity. The production on figure 4 should be compared both with productions on other figures in which either straight lines or curved lines or both are present, in order to derive suitable hypotheses, and with the elaboration and association data for confirmation of these hypotheses and the development of new hypotheses to account for all of the data. A great variety of relevant inferences can be derived from this figure alone as well as from a comparison with the patient's productions on preceding figures. Note, for example, how this is done with some of the cases presented in Chapters VII through XI, and XIII.

Figure 5 is another open figure composed of dots. Several of the most pertinent phenomena associated with this figure will be discussed briefly. Rotation frequently occurs for the first time because of the perceptual valence of the secant which forces some patients to rotate the entire figure; they are unable to resist the inertia created by the angulated secant and consequently rotate the entire figure. Another feature is the tendency to complete the circle by extending the circular portion of the figure. This phenomenon is usually associated with feelings of insecurity and dependence. Simplification may also occur as still another defensive maneuver. Obsessive-compulsive patients frequently count the dots over and over again, sometimes losing the Gestalt while trying to reproduce the number of dots accurately. The relative size of the secant should be examined for the deduction of any of a number of hypotheses, such as: paranoid features (elaboration or overextension of the size of the secant—because of its phallic characteristics); authority problems (decrease in the vertical dimension of the total figure with foreshortening of the secant); passivity as a reaction formation to hostile wishes (decrease of the secant together with a wavy line quality). Simplification of the figure may be attempted by reducing markedly the total number of dots or by substituting a curved line for the semicircle of dots or by using lines in place of dots for the entire figure (see Chapter X).

The next figure, number 6, coming as it does after a succession of previous figures and representing such a direct portrayal of emotionality, is another important figure in sequential and inferential analysis. Not only does the curvature present problems to some patients but the intersection of two sets of curves in a nonsymmetrical manner aggravates the problem for many. Patients who are able to maintain a facade of appropriate affectivity but whose affective behavior is not spontaneous have great difficulty here. The various phenomena which may result are highly revealing. Are the curves flattened (reduction of the emotional value of the stimulus), are they spiked (difficulty in holding aggressive drives under check), or are they reduced in number or amplitude (affective withdrawal)? Again, are the two curves made to intersect at right angles or are the curves drawn with considerable evidence of motor incoordination (inability to handle the "hot" emotional meaning of these stimuli). Some patients draw the two curves not as intersecting but as two tangential "U" curves—an important indication of marked fearfulness in interpersonal relations. Depressive features sometimes appear for the first time on this figure (mild clockwise rotation, light wavy lines, and similar

features). Paranoid characteristics sometimes become evident (the elaboration of the curve as the profile of a face, or the insertion of a dot for an eye,
for example). Patients with markedly impulsive characteristics will frequently increase the size of the curves greatly and will use excessive line
pressure. The highly anxious but intact patient may, on the other hand,
diminish the size of the curves and draw them with light pressure and sketchy
lines.

As is well known by now, figure 7 offers the most clear-cut evidence of the
presence of organicity in the patient (difficulty with overlapping) but it offers
many other leads as well. With respect to the problem of intracranial damage
it should be emphasized that overlapping difficulty may be evidenced in
very many different ways. The most obvious of these is the failure to reproduce the overlapping Gestalt. Other, less obvious ways are: sketching at
the point of overlap of the two figures; severe rotation of the figures; marked
difficulty with some of the angles (especially if none was noted on such
figures as A and 4); simplification of either or both parts of the figure; overlap at an incorrect point; marked overshooting in the closure at any of the
apexes; substitution of curved for straight lines; total destruction of the
Gestalt. The phallic quality of this Gestalt, and the threat to some types of
homosexuals, should not be overlooked. This type of reaction to the symbolic
meaning of the stimulus figure can be checked against the reaction obtained
with figure 8, about which more will be said below. When the phallic quality
is too threatening to the patient he may defend against this in a number of
ways, such as rounding off any of the upper or lower apexes of the figures,
decreasing the length of the figures or increasing their width, or by shortening
the extreme sections of the figures. Sometimes, patients with severe superego
problems and guilt over fantasied sexual perversions or excesses separate the
two figures or simplify them; in such cases the evidence of overt anxiety noted
in this and other figures will help to differentiate this type of difficulty from
that of organicity. Figure 7 also lends itself to rather clear manifestation of
other types of anxieties and difficulties in interpersonal relations, evidenced
by such phenomena as closure difficulties, crossing difficulties, variations in
line quality, difficulties with angles, rotational problems, and the like.

Figure 8 is also reacted to, very frequently, in terms of its sexual, and
particularly its phallic, qualities.[38] One of the interesting findings is that
individuals with conflict over homosexuality (and young adults or adolescents
with conflict over masturbation) have difficulties with the extremities of this
figure. The most usual distortions involve production of the two extremities
in markedly different sizes, difficulties with the angles in the extremities,
substitution of curved lines for the straight lines in the extreme portions of
the figure, and excessive sketching. Another feature to which special attention

should be given is the production of the internal diamond. Difficulty with this portion of the figure may involve reduction in size, misplacement in position (off-center), or difficulty in closure or joining either of parts of the diamond or of the diamond with the sides of the hexagon. Such difficulties are usually associated with conflict with the female sex and fearfulness in connection with intercourse. It is instructive to note, when such types of distortions occur, whether similar difficulties have been experienced in connection with the square (or diamond) in figure A. It will sometimes be noted that no significant distortions occur in figure A but are quite marked in figure 8. There may be many reasons to account for this, but the two most common explanations are that: figure 8 is the last in the test and reflects the cumulative anxieties which have been built up in the course of the examination, and figure 8 seems to evoke more directly some of the conflicts related to sexual relationships. Confirmation of either of these (or other) explanations for this figure may often be obtained during the elaboration and association phases of the test.

If the clinician has been following our suggestions for developing inferences from the responses to the copy phase of the test he will have developed many explanations and hunches concerning the patient, he will have revised and extended some of these, and he will have rejected others in the light of a more parsimonious explanation that became available. Further, utilizing his knowledge concerning personality theory and psychopathology he will have developed a general personality conceptualization concerning the specific patient. On the basis of such leads a number of second order inferences can then be developed. However, if data are available from the elaboration and association phases of the test, it would be well to examine these data before attempting to integrate these second order hypotheses.

We have already discussed the rationale for the procedures of the *elaboration* and *association phases* of the test in Chapters III and IV. At this point we wish merely to emphasize certain features of these rationales.

In the first place, the motoric activity involved in the process of elaborating the Gestalt figures, especially since ego controls are relaxed somewhat by the instruction "modify the figures . . . so as to make them more pleasing," tends to produce both exaggeration of underlying and relatively more unconscious processes and associations and material (traumatic) associated with the anal and oedipal phases of development (the periods of "socialization"). Consistencies in distortions first found in the *copy phase* and later exaggerated in the *elaboration phase* are therefore of special interest. But also of interest are new types of distortions which occur only on the *elaboration phase*. These consistencies and new types of evidence can be evaluated more completely in terms of the associations given by the patient to both the *copy phase* and the *elaboration phase* material. Although we have stressed the capacity of these procedures to elicit material from anal and phallic phases, other phases of development may be projected in these materials, for example, such obvious "oral" associations to figure 6 as "a fountain" or "sucking movements."

Sometimes patients will reveal "sudden insights" concerning material they have produced during the *elaboration phase*. They will verbalize, with surprise, that they didn't know just what they were doing, or they were just "doodling," but now it is very clear that the figure means "such and such." Often, they will insist that no other explanation is possible; i.e., because of the intensity of the projection, they will have "lost distance" from their productions and can entertain no alternative explanations. Sometimes, they will exclaim that the association is something they had forgotten or had never thought about before. Such kinds of verbal behavior are important evidence of the intrinsic validity of the productions—although, of course, any clinician will realize that sometimes the most apparently valid recollections are but screen memories.

In analyzing the elaboration data, it is suggested that the general rules offered for developing hypotheses in connection with the *copy phase* data be followed. First, it is desirable to analyze the general stylistic features of the total set of elaboration productions, and then it is well to analyze the separate productions in the sequence in which they were offered. Also, the same general procedures for entertaining apparently contradictory hypotheses until the evidence forces a selection or integration of the explanations is considered desirable. Only after the elaboration material has been analyzed in this manner is it desirable to compare the implications of the *elaboration* with the *copy phase* hypotheses in detail.

Configurational Analysis

In this section we shall present evidence concerning configurations associated with a number of nosologic, psychiatric categories. We wish to emphasize, however, that we should *not* expect very high correlations between specific configurations and specific nosologic entities for reasons already specified in Chapter III. Moreover, since each nosologic category is simply a constellation of *commonly occurring derivative behavior* (symptoms), we should expect to find considerable variance in underlying process phenomena which have given rise to such behavior. And, finally, there is the implicit assumption that there is some essential homogeneity in the conditions underlying each nosologic category, an assumption which we believe is highly suspect in some instances. For example, there is mounting evidence that the various conditions which have been grouped together for a number of decades under the general rubric of schizophrenia may represent quite different underlying processes instead of a single unitary "disease" process.

Although the configurations which we are about to present have been "validated" by many years of clinical experience, by a number of experiments in which "blind" diagnosis was attempted, and by some experimental studies, much remains to be done before they (or modifications of them) can be considered as reliable. Moreover, additional data are needed to determine whether or not there are significant sex differences. (The configurations may, for the time being, be assumed to be more valid for males than for females.) Many other types of studies are also needed to determine such relationships, if any, between types of RBGT configurations and types of socioeconomic categories, duration of the psychiatric condition, and the like.

It will be noted that each configuration is divided into two parts, the first section giving the most common concurrence of findings, and the second section giving frequently associated findings. It is considered that the phenomena in the first section contain the *essential discriminators* for that general nosologic category, while the phenomena in the second section contain material found in a number of nosologic categories. We assume that there are, therefore, some group factors and some more general indicators of psychiatric disturbance, but no factors which are entirely specific to only one nosologic group. The first section of the configuration, entitled *essential discriminators*, tends to distinguish that category from all others. A rough rule of thumb is that the presence of *five or more* of the phenomena in the *essential* group is sufficient to merit the diagnostic categorization of that group. When a particular record presents five or more findings for more than one group, one can assume that the patient presents a mixed condition and is not entirely characterized by one nosologic grouping. It should also be remembered that the particular form of the general nosologic category which appropriately describes a particular patient must be determined from either an inferential analysis of the RBGT or from other types of clinical evidence, or both. Perhaps when our psychiatric nosologies are better defined (in terms of underlying process phenomena instead of clusters of symptoms) a more valid and rigorous configurational summary will be possible. Meanwhile, it is believed that greater reliance on methods of inferential than on configurational analysis seems warranted.

A. *Classical or Essential Psychoneurosis* (Exclusive of Character Disorder)
  1. ESSENTIAL DISCRIMINATORS
     a. Sequence: either overly methodical or irregular.
     b. Space: either excessive or constricted.
     c. Margin: excessive use.
     d. Size: over-all increase or (especially) decrease.

    e. Size: marked increase or decrease in parts of designs.

    f. Closure difficulty: especially if present on two or more figures.

    g. Crossing difficulty: figures 6 and 7.

    h. Curvature difficulty.

    i. Angulation difficulty: either increase or decrease.

    j. Rotation difficulty: mild (especially with depressives).

    k. Movement difficulty: inconsistency in direction.

2. ASSOCIATED DISCRIMINATORS

    a. Placement, first figure: abnormal (especially in upper left-hand corner, hugging the margin together with decreased size).

    b. Shift in position of paper.

    c. Size: progressive increase or decrease.

    d. Doodling: especially when anxiety is high and overt.

    e. Perseveration: type B only (usually on only one figure).

    f. Line quality: occasional, very heavy or very light lines, accompanied by some evidence of incoordination.

    g. Overt behavioral resistance.

    h. Counting: excessive (especially with impulse problems and with phobic individuals).

B. *Intracranial Damage* (The phenomena will vary markedly, depending on the type of damage, previous personality, duration of the deficit, and the like.)

1. ESSENTIAL DISCRIMINATORS

    a. Rotation: severe (especially when present without awareness and when patient has great difficulty in correcting or cannot correct).

    b. Overlapping difficulty.

    c. Simplification.

    d. Fragmentation.

    e. Retrogression.

    f. Perseveration: especially type B.

    g. Collision difficulty or tendency.

    h. Impotence: initial expressions of impotence and other behavioral evidence of impotence such as repetitive drawings of figures with similar inaccuracies.

    i. Closure difficulty: if marked and if persistent.

    j. Motor incoordination.

    k. Angulation difficulty: if severe (especially on figure 2).

    l. Cohesion or isolated decrease in size (factor 10), especially on figure 3.

2. ASSOCIATED DISCRIMINATORS

    a. Sketching difficulty.

    b. Size: marked reduction in size.

    c. Sequence: irregular to confused.

     d. Compensatory angulation (especially on figure 2).

     e. Crossing difficulty.

     f. Sketching.

     g. Impulsivity.

C. *Schizophrenia*

  1. ESSENTIAL DISCRIMINATORS

     a. Sequence: confused or symbolic (infrequent in paranoid and uncomplicated, simple forms of schizophrenia).

     b. Placement, first figure: in abnormal position.

     c. Space: very uneven use of space.

     d. Collision tendency.

     e. Shift in position of stimulus cards: if very pronounced.

     f. Angulation: if severe.

     g. Rotation: severe (usually accompanied by awareness).

     h. Retrogression: if present in two or more figures.

     i. Fragmentation: especially separation into discrete parts.

     j. Simplification.

     k. Cohesion or isolated decrease in lateral size: usually marked, when present.

     l. Doodling: usually marked, when present, and may have symbolic meaning to patient.

  2. ASSOCIATED DISCRIMINATORS

     a. Perseveration: type A; more infrequently, type B.

     b. Curvature: marked decrease (less frequently, marked increase).

     c. Crossing difficulty.

     d. Direction of movement: marked inconsistencies.

     e. Progressive increase in size: marked.

     f. Margin: excessive hugging of margin.

     g. Frank elaboration of sexual symbols.

D. *Mental Retardation.* Mental retardation may be accompanied by and is sometimes the result of severe emotional disturbance from an early age, resulting in withdrawal and cognitive inhibition. Hence, analysis will be made of both retardation of mental development and of evidence of emotional disturbance. When adults suspected of mental retardation perform relatively better on figures 7 and 8 than on figures A and 4, emotional factors are likely to be highly significant.

  1. ESSENTIAL DISCRIMINATORS

     a. Sequence: irregular.

     b. Position of first figure: abnormal (frequently in center of page).

     c. Space: highly irregular.

     d. Collision: usually only collision tendencies.

     e. Size: usually increased size.

     f. Angulation: changes are usually irregular.

     g. Rotation: moderate or else complete reversal.

     h. Simplification.

     i. Fragmentation: but incomplete, and only on the more difficult figures.

     j. Perseveration: type A, but no anxiety manifested.

     k. Difficulty with figures 7 and 8 (on angles and with overlapping on figure 7).

  2. ASSOCIATED DISCRIMINATORS

     a. Closure difficulty: marked, when present.

     b. Crossing difficulty.

     c. Movement: inconsistent direction of movement.

     d. Doodling: aimless and nonsymbolic.

     e. Curvature: usually flattened.

E. *Manic States.* There are some theoretical issues regarding the etiology of manic states, particularly in terms of the degree of regression, if any, and fragmentation of the ego. More likely, mania is a *reactive condition* rather than a process disorder as illustrated by certain forms of schizophrenia. Though mania has been traditionally classified as a psychosis, contemporary thinking has advanced the thesis that it represents a transient reactive process with marked characterologic components. Our configurational findings are to be associated with reactive conditions, therefore. Other types of manic behavior may be associated with a schizophrenic process or with other types of psychopathologies.

  1. ESSENTIAL DISCRIMINATORS

     a. Sequence: irregular to confused.

     b. Space: excessive, particularly type II; typically, large amounts of paper are utilized.

     c. Size: markedly increased.

     d. Doodling.

     e. Rotation: counterclockwise direction.

     f. Impulsive work habits.

  2. ASSOCIATED DISCRIMINATORS

     a. Closure difficulty.

     b. Collision difficulty or collision tendency.

     c. Curvature: usually increased.

     d. Angulation: usually increased.

F. *Character Disorders.* These disorders are so varied that it is difficult, if not impossible, to present a configuration that discriminates them from other clinical problems as well as from each other. The clinician, in interpreting a RBGT record, must consequently look for configurational factors that are consistent with the general classes of psychopathology which differentiate the character disorder; namely: that they represent enduring and characteristic modes of adaptation by the individual to his environment which are both pathologic and ego-syntonic. Two general subclasses of character disorder are also differentiated: those in which impulses are freely expressed and those in which impulses are markedly inhibited.[26]

PART II

VII

Case Illustration: Psychotic Records

The material which is presented in Chapters VII through XI is intended to exemplify the methods and problems which have been discussed in Part I. The treatment of the material in these chapters varies. In some chapters (VII, X, and XI) only the copy phase material of the RBGT and summary statements of the clinical diagnosis are given. In the others, additional RBGT data are presented and discussed and more detailed consideration is given to other psychometric and clinical findings. It is hoped that this varied presentation of RBGT data will indicate some of the possible ways in which such material can be utilized. Sometimes, in clinical work, there is insufficient time to obtain a full RBGT record and insufficient time to carry through an elaborate clinical analysis. The shorter case presentations will indicate what can be done with even a limited amount of data and with limited time for analysis.

It is expected, of course, that some workers will wish to score the RBGT in accordance with some scheme like that of Pascal and Suttel's[33] or in accordance with some methods like those reviewed in Chapters II and V of the present work. Scoring of this kind has its important functions, particularly in research studies, but it does not add as much as would be desirable to the individual clinical picture. Moreover, a general score based on some type of summary of all test factors is probably less useful than a score or series of scores designed to test specific hypotheses. Our discussion in Chapter II pointed up the special values of studies like those of Byrd,[6] Clawson,[7] and Story[37] in which specific hypotheses were tested on the basis of specialized scores for parts of the record. Similarly, in clinical work, the psychologist may wish only to test specific hypotheses with respect to a particular patient; i.e., are there indications of an organic factor for this patient, or is there evidence of a psychotic process, or is this a case of simple mental retardation or one in which emotional conflicts have produced severe cognitive inhibition? The cases which follow should provide sufficient samples to allow each worker to examine RBGT data with respect to highly restricted hypotheses or with respect to general personality problems which may be indicated.

95

We shall now present two cases in which different types of emphases in the analysis are offered. In the first case, the RBGT was submitted for analysis to one of the authors for a "blind" analysis as part of an over-all clinical and research study. The report which was submitted indicates the principles and methods of *inferential analysis* discussed in Chapter VI. This first case is also interesting because it involves an individual whose psychiatric diagnosis was quite complicated and the problems of differential diagnosis are therefore of considerable importance. We shall call this first case, Case A. The second case, that of a well-enucleated schizophrenic, is presented with a different orientation. In this instance we wish to illustrate some of the phenomena which are characteristic of RBGT records and merely to call attention to the presence of several test factors and to the *configurational* findings. We shall call this Case B.

Case A

The RBGT record of this 25 year old individual is presented in Plate 4. The record was obtained as part of a psychological evaluation and was then given to one of the present authors with only the information summarized in the first paragraph of the interpretation. The interpretation is quoted exactly as it was presented and published in the volume by Shneidman (ref. 25, pp. 227-233). Following the summary, we shall comment briefly on the problems which this record presents and on the clinical and therapeutic findings which were later made available and summarized in the Shneidman volume.

It shall not be our purpose to discuss the types of qualifications one must bear in mind in discussing this record, qualifications arising from a situation in which the interpreter is in ignorance of such things as the nature of the setting in which this examination was administered, the sequence of tests and/or therapy preceding the test, the nature of the interpersonal relation, and the like. This interpreter had the following data at his disposal: the test record (photographic reproductions) and some very brief notes on methods of work (both of which are included with this record of interpretation); these limited identification data: age, 25 years; sex, male; marital status, single; education, high school; handedness, left; no gross physical limitations.

Our first "general" inspection of the test protocol reveals the following: the drawings are arranged in "correct" sequence from A, the introductory design, to 8, the last design, and the patient "lines" his drawings up along the left margin until he has reached the bottom of the sheet, then proceeds by "completing the available space," introducing design 7 to the right of and under design 2, and follows this, again in sequence and in the vertical plane, with the last design. We note further that design A is attempted in

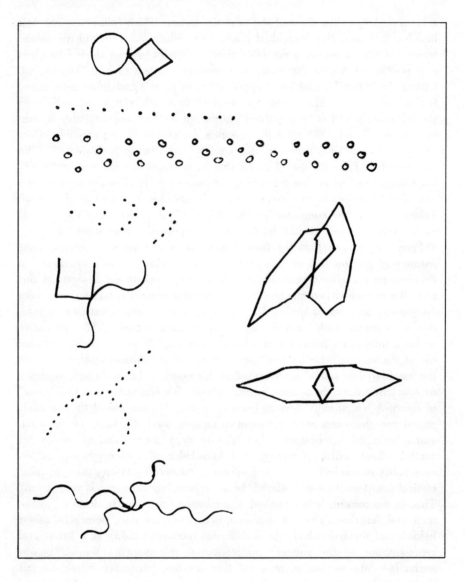

PLATE 4   A Psychotic Record.

a locus slightly to the right of the next six designs which follow it. Our first hunches then are: this individual has strong orderly, i.e., compulsive, needs, tending toward a sort of compulsive ritual, but tries to deny them (the aberrant position of A plus the examiner's comment on this design, "Draws fast, without hesitation"), and he is oppressed with some (probably) generalized feelings of anxiety and (more specifically) personal inadequacy (clings to the left margin and is "constrained" to use all of the space available to him on this one sheet). We raise the question for consideration, at once, "How strong and from what source is this anxiety and what is his defense?" We can speculate, from his use of space, that he attempts in some way to "bind" his anxiety, i.e., he cannot tolerate it for long or in large amounts, and that one of the features of this young adult's functioning is the need of control. Taken together, the compulsivity, the "binding" of anxiety, and the need of control offer the first general inference: the superego is very strict.

Permit us to interrupt the formal analysis at this point to review some features of our method of interpretation, since what we have attempted to demonstrate thus far is characteristic of our approach to the analysis of this test. We examined two main features of the test record: spatial arrangement (sequence) and use of the total space area. We correlated extreme orderliness of sequence with compulsivity in functioning (based on the normative findings from our clinical samples from young adults) and the fairly extreme use of the margin with anxiety (again a normative clinical finding). These are considered *tentative* formulations at this point, to be confirmed, modified or rejected in the light of subsequent analysis. We also noted that the "locus" of figure A was slightly deviant from the others (in the use of the margin), considered the examiner's comment regarding subject's haste in drawing, and offered the implication: "but tries to deny them," i.e., his needs for control. Next, utilizing our general knowledge of pathology (or, better, personality dynamics), we tried to speculate concerning the meaning of these clinical manifestations and offered the *inference:* "the superego is very strict." This, in microcosm, is our method of analyzing traits, needs, defenses, symptoms and function. The test is a sample of the nonverbal, perceptual-motor behavior of the individual. As such it has intrinsic validity as a behavioral representation of the patient's adaptation at the moment. We utilize our normative data as cues to interpretation for this particular sample of this particular individual. Some of the cues may appear to be contradictory; others may supplement and confirm each other. The clinical task is to make meaning not only of the cues but their interrelationships and, based on the frame of reference for all humans from a similar population (i.e., the personality dynamics of young, American, ostensibly white, high school graduate adults, in this case), to predict the underlying kind of personality which could be responsible for this total production.

Returning now to the test record, we examine figure A more carefully. The size is slightly smaller than the original. The horizontal axis of the figure is rotated slightly in a clockwise direction. These suggest: fear (self-critical attitude) and depressive reaction, respectively. Both figures are of proportionate size (no specific, exaggerated reaction to either male or female sex symbol), but, perhaps, the moderate rotation of the horizontal axis of the total figure is due to a specific reaction (dread of, hostility toward or lack of identification with, the male parent or surrogate). The latter possibility, or a derivative of it, is supported by the difficulty in "joining" the two figures (exaggerated, redrawn, overemphasized junction of the figures). This point is the more likely to be significant in view of the patient's speed in drawing and in view of the apparently impulsive, concave sides of the square.

Figure 1, the twelve dots, is also drawn fast, with "no checking back on number of dots," the examiner notes. The number of dots is correct (confirms the patient's need for exactness, i.e., his compulsive trend), but the line of dots is wavy, the dots are filled in, and they are somewhat uneven in size and intensity. Here again, we find the apparent dilemma proposed above: the patient is compulsive but attempts to deny it. For a person who arranges his drawings on the page so methodically this "carelessness" in the alignment and size of the dots is striking. Perhaps he perceives the task of figure 1 as too simple to require careful effort. His tendency toward "haste" on all of the drawings suggests: impulsivity or a derogatory attitude toward the test or inner tension which is flowing over. The fact that the dots are heavily (and unevenly) filled in suggests that it is the last alternative which fits best. General, tentative inference: high aspiration level in a tense individual unable to accept simple experiences as nonchallenging. It is also worth noting that the dots tend to follow a downward trend: depressive reaction.

Figure 2, the ten diagonal columns of circles, offers further evidence of the marked variability which begins to appear to be characteristic of this patient. The examiner notes, "Checks number of rows (i.e., columns) about two-thirds through." We note that the angles of the columns of dots differ, becoming more obtuse (from the vertical) with a correction toward the end. The whole figure is exaggerated in the lateral plane. Together, these findings suggest a strong need to relate to people, but difficulty in establishing such relationships. The orientation of the first column is correct, so the variation in "angulation" is not a simple perceptual difficulty. The patient gets the number of columns correct, but varies both angulation and spacing. We have evidence, then, for the presence of considerable internal tension with an attempt at denial of its existence. How can we explain the apparent contradiction of the need for order and control with the speed and variability of performance? His compulsive defenses do not function effectively enough. In addition to the postulation of his impulsivity, we must add some mechanism which permits him to react so emotionally, i.e., so violently. This is especially necessary in view of "collision tendency" (figures 1 and 2). We therefore think of "acting-out," a mechanism in which ego controls are cut off (cease to function temporarily) and regressive impulsivity breaks through. If this is indeed the case, we can argue that superego demands can be side-stepped, guilt is temporarily overcome only to return in increasing intensity once the ego is later able to survey the transgression. This would thereby satisfy the patient's masochistic needs (to expiate his guilt) and thus serve a doubly useful purpose. Another possibility, which we should like to consider, is that of psychotic episodes, but the evidence for this in the record is lacking (there is no indication of a full-fledged psychotic process in the record), so we abandon this for the more parsimonious explanation already given.

Figure 3 is elongated laterally, a further indication of the patient's attempt to relate to others. The dissociation of the parts of the "arrowhead" supports the possibility of the "acting-out" mechanism offered above. The downward orientation of the figure again suggests depressive reaction. The correct number of dots and the intensity of the dots indicate: orderliness (i.e., compulsive trend) and inner tenson. The Gestalt is accurate, although, again, in the segment consisting of five dots, the "postmark" of impulsivity is revealed. The increase in the horizontal dimension of the figure is accompanied by a decrease in the vertical dimension; is he fearful of authority figures?

In figure 4, the patient has increased the vertical sides of the open square; (there are no notes by the examiner); this is deduced from the "breaks" occurring in both vertical lines. His reaction to authority figures can now be inferred more completely: he is hostile to such figures, unable to express his hostility directly, and reacts either symbolically or impulsively. In line with the "acting-out" hypothesis, the former is more likely. The curved portion of this figure is enlarged, flattened out in the middle, and reveals an impulsive flourish at the upper end. Now we may speculate that his major identification is with a female figure, but she is perceived as more masculine (i.e., dominant, aggressive) than feminine and is reacted to openly with antagonism. It is interesting that the upper portion of the curved figure extends well above its position on the stimulus card, and is at least as high up as the vertical lines. Here we may conjecture that his mother (or surrogate) was stronger psychologically than his father, or at least seemed so to him, and that he would like to use his mother (or women) to defy his father (or men).

The depressive coloring in the patient's attempt at figure 5 is striking (clockwise orientation of the total figure). He has difficulty with the projecting line of dots, attaching it about midway on the circumference of the "semicircle" of dots, although it is off-center on the stimulus. Despite this, other features of the drawing are precisely accurate: the number of dots in the "semicircle," the number of dots in the projection, and the position between the seventh and eighth dot of the circumference for the point of union. Here is, indeed, compulsive attention to detail, despite which, the figure in toto is distorted. If we accept the premise that this figure "stands for" the mother surrogate, we may then infer that his vehemence against this symbol can be, and is, expressed in an open-structured figure, while he cannot so distort it in the simpler, more conventional symbolism of figure A. Again, this would support the premise of a symbolic acting-out of his conflict with his mother (and with women), although conventionally he is deferent, obedient, and conformist.

Figure 6, the sinusoidal curves, taxes him to the utmost. Affect is strong (amplitude of curves), but is expressed unevenly (uneven wave lengths). Marked difficulty occurs at the crossing. (E's notes support this.) The excessive loop at the top of the vertical curve plus the fact that this curve was drawn first, from the top down, express the patient's suppressed hostility to male, parental symbols. The Gestalt is accurate, but the difficulty with this figure is apparent in the drawing. One would expect this patient to show some apathy in his typical behavior, but react on occasion with outbursts, probably of a sexual, or, better, sexual-symbolic, character.

On figure 7, the right-hand figure is rotated slightly in a clockwise direction and all of the joinings show "closure difficulty." There is an exaggeration of the lower section of the left-hand figure. The Gestalt is accurate. We infer: depressive reactions; difficulty in maintaining interpersonal relations; feelings of sexual inadequacy (possibly feelings of impotence).

The same closure difficulty is noted on figure 8, on which E says, "Draws small inside diamond first, then encloses." The figure is increased in size laterally and the ends are exaggerated. Inferences: difficulty in interpersonal relations; major identification with female figures; sexual impotency (or fear thereof).

One final observation: the spacing between successive figures is constricted. This fits in with our conception of him as essentially anal in fixation and generally suppressive of conscious hostility feelings.

From all of the above, we may attempt to etch out the personality as it functions on this psychological task, and offer some predictions to be considered in the light of other data.

We would suspect that this individual tries to give the impression of a sophisticated, but conforming, individual. He has unusually high aspirations, but feels limited and inadequate, although ordinarily denying this to others and attempting to deny it to himself. He is subject to marked inner turmoil, but attempts to conceal this, too, from others and himself. His ambition and drive toward achievement, and in general his compulsive controls offer some compensation, but they are not enough. He suffers from melancholy and intense feelings of frustration. He finds it increasingly difficult to work effectively. At the root of his difficulty lies an identification with a dominant, and to him, unrewarding mother-figure, toward whom he reacts with some hostility, but toward whom he is very attracted sexually. For some reason (the record is not indicative) he is also fearful (and unable to express it) toward the father-figure. We may speculate that the father is perceived as strong but ineffectual in relation to the mother (for some reason) and that he has guilt over his attraction to the mother, who is objective, strong, just, but unobtainable. With this nucleus in this type of oedipal conflict as a base, his development was attended by deep guilt reactions stirred by a strict superego development. A relatively strong ego enabled him to move along for a time until late adolescent and young adult situational factors decreased the effectiveness of ego functions, at least for a time. It is suggested that then either Don Juan behavior or symbolic acting-out occurred (possibly both), and guilt increased until the prevalent masochistic pattern was re-established. One would suspect that depressive reactions, possibly suicidal preoccupation, began as the cycle became tighter and as the vocational-occupational sublimations became less effective with decreased efficiency in total functioning. The Don Juan hypothesis is in line with the speculation that he tried to act out his needs for masculine competence in the face of increasing feelings of sexual inadequacy and guilt. The anchorage of good, intense relationships with peers is lacking, although wished for.

Superficially, this young man may give the impression of control and fair effectiveness. If our speculations concerning the nature of his difficulties are substantially correct, we may suggest that he will be able to make very effective use of analytically oriented therapy, providing this is both intensive and fairly extensive.

The above analysis of a record attempts to present an illustration of *inferential analysis*. We can evaluate it in terms of effectiveness against the extensive clinical and treatment findings which Shneidman subsequently presented in his volume.[25]

Insofar as basic dynamics are concerned, the RBGT analysis comes remarkably close to the findings of this man's therapist; not only are the statements of the nature of the conflicts and their attempted resolution the same or very similar, but even the rhetorical phrasing of the problem in the RBGT report and in the report of the therapist is very similar, almost identical.

It might also be pointed out that the report of the psychology staff of the hospital where this man was under study and treatment, based upon a battery of tests and interviews, also arrived at findings essentially similar to those of the analysis based on the RBGT.

Specifically, the psychiatric history indicated that this man, a patient in a neuropsychiatric hospital, was admitted with the following symptoms: insomnia, palpitation, night sweats, trembling when people observed him, and feelings of inadequacy. His difficulties were reported as having begun some six months after he entered the Navy, in which he was assigned to the medical corps. Since his discharge his concentration had become quite poor and his symptoms had increased progressively.

At the hospital he was first diagnosed as: psychoneurosis, anxiety type, acute and severe. Later, psychiatric consultation suggested that he was most likely an obsessive-compulsive, but that the diagnosis was "between obsessive-compulsive neurosis, anxiety-hysteria and schizophrenia." The discharge diagnosis was that of anxiety reaction.

Following discharge from the hospital, the patient was seen in therapy at a mental hygiene clinic. The patient terminated therapy, conducted by a psychiatric case worker under close psychiatric consultation. The closing note on this case may be of interest. "The material obtained seemed to indicate more and more clearly that his defenses were crumbling and that he was either close to a psychotic break or actually psychotic. . . . Diagnosis: schizophrenic reaction, paranoid type."

We cannot take the space to review the specific dynamic findings of the therapist which confirmed those of the RBGT, but the interested reader may study these for himself in the fairly exhaustive summary which Shneidman presents.[25]

Case B

This is the case of a male, white patient, 38 years of age, hospitalized for severe personality disturbance because of inability to maintain himself in society and who had periods of violent acting-out. He was diagnosed as chronic, undifferentiated schizophenia, and it was estimated that the outbreak of the psychotic reaction had occurred some 10 years before. Plate 5 presents his responses on the *copy phase* of the RBGT. As we have already indicated, we shall simply note some of the test factors which characterize this record and comment on the nature of his configuration.

Sequence. This falls within the category of methodical sequence since only two figures indicate a deviation from a regular pattern (a deviation after figure 3 and another after figure 5). Thus, sequence is atypical for schizophrenia.

Position of the first drawing. The placement of figure A is clearly atypical or abnormal.

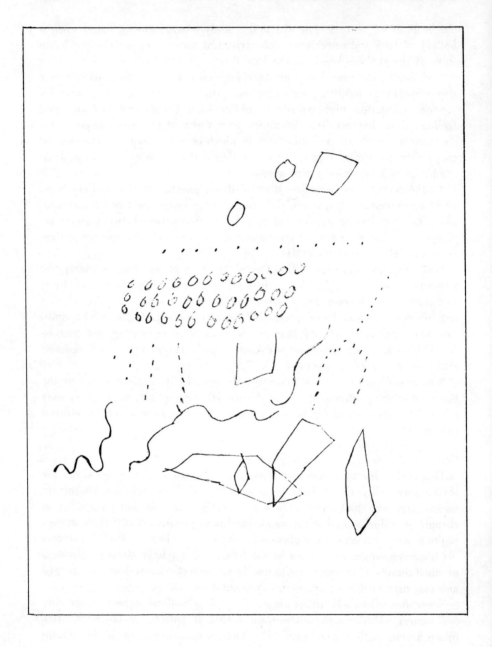

PLATE 5   Another Psychotic Record.

Use of space I. The record must be characterized as constricted. Moreover, spacing is very uneven.

Use of space II. Again, this is a constricted record. In both aspects of the use of space this record is clearly atypical and is consistent with the configurational findings for schizophrenia.

Collision. An actual, but slight, collision occurs between figures 3 and 4, and 7 and 8, and collision tendencies occur on other figures, e.g., 2 and 3, 3 and 6, and 4 and 5. These findings are consistent with the configuration for schizophrenia.

Use of margin. This factor is not present. Except in schizophrenics with intense anxiety or in incipent stages of this disorder, this factor is not likely to be present.

Shift in the position of the paper. This does not occur.

Shift in position of the stimulus cards. There is no notation in the examiner's notes of this phenomenon.

Over-all change in size. This record does not meet the criteria for this test factor.

Progressive change in size. This is not present.

Isolated change in size. This factor is clearly present. It will be noted that the circle in figure A, for example, is disproportionately small in relation to the square. Similarly, one part of figure 6 is disproportionately small. Although this factor has not been included within the configuration presented in Chapter VI for schizophrenia, it is significant in evaluating the dynamics of the individual case.

Closure difficulty. This is present and very pronounced. This finding is not unique to schizophrenia, by any means, but again, in inferential analysis it would be of importance.

Crossing difficulty. This factor is present for both figures 6 and 7. It is an associated discriminator in schizophrenia.

Curvature difficulty. Flattening occurs in figure 4. Both irregularity and flattening occur in figure 6. These are the most pronounced indications of curvature difficulty in this record. The finding is consistent with schizophrenia as an associated discriminator.

Change in angulation. This is present on figure 2 (the decreased angulation of the columns of circles), on figure 3, on figure 7, and on figure 8. The defenses of this patient against emotional impact of the stimuli represented by these figures may be inferred.

Rotation. Mild rotation occurs on figures 5 and 6. Moderate rotation occurs on figure 8. This factor is of borderline significance in this record with respect to schizophrenia.

Retrogression. This is marked. Note the dashes in figure 3 and the pronounced difficulties in figures 7 and 8. The presence of this factor in two or more figures is consistent with the diagnosis of schizophrenia.

Simplification. This also is marked. It may be noted in figures A, 3, 4, 6, 7, and 8. This is still another essential discriminator for schizophrenia.

Fragmentation. This factor is present in figures A, 4, 6, and 8. Again, this is an essential discriminator for schizophrenia.

Overlapping difficulty. Present on all three criterion figures: 4, 6, and 7.

Elaboration or doodling. Not present.

Perseveration. This may be present in figure A, in which the circle is repeated; it may also be noted in figure 2 (the excessive number of columns), and is present in figure 6. However, these perseverative tendencies (type B) are not pronounced, nor is the other type of perseveration (type A) present. Perseverative tendencies, particularly of type B, are much more marked in organic records, but we can suggest that this record is not likely to be that of an organic, on this and on other bases.

The test record alone is insufficient to judge the test factor of *line movement,* and there is no clear indication of any significant disturbance in the factors of *line quality.*

An examination of the above analysis will indicate that this record contains seven clear indicators of the schizophrenic configuration (essential discriminators), one doubtful indicator of this type, and at least two of the associated discriminators. Thus, the findings are consistent with the diagnostic categorization of schizophrenia, process type. Of course, in the analysis of an individual case, careful attention would be given to other factors in the RBGT record as well as to other types of analyses, including inferential analysis. However, this presentation may suffice to indicate the possibilities of relatively simple configurational analysis.

VIII

Case Illustration: A Neurotic Record

The case presented here was chosen to illustrate two aspects of the RBGT: a modification in administration, and the richness of the record.

John, as we shall call him, had been referred by his psychiatrist who had a number of questions concerning the nature of his problems and this patient's suitability for psychotherapy. John had sought the help of the psychiatrist at the urging of his wife who felt that her husband was showing increasing difficulties in holding down a job and who wished assistance for John with his problem of alcoholism. She stated that their marital relationship had never been entirely satisfactory but that John had been a good provider and that he was considerate. John was not sure that he needed psychotherapy, admitted to periods when he felt tense and irritable, explained that he was getting bored with his job and that he drank, only on occasion, to relieve his feelings of boredom and tension. The psychiatrist, who had seen John for a short consultation, wondered how "sick" John might be and how well motivated he was for psychotherapy. John was 48 years old at the time of examination. His wife was 35 years of age.

John was quite cooperative during the psychological examination. He appeared obviously tense and a mild expressive aphasia was suspected on the basis of his speech patterns. Mood was slightly depressed, but judgment and memory appeared to be unimpaired. He gave the impression of being somewhat passive and compliant.

Plate 6 contains the record of the *copy phase* of the RBGT. It will be noted that only six figures were presented. This was done to save time, since only one visit by this patient was available and sufficient time was needed during this visit to administer a Rorschach test. Clinical experience has indicated that figures A, 2, 4, 6, 7, and 8 furnish a very good sample of all of

107

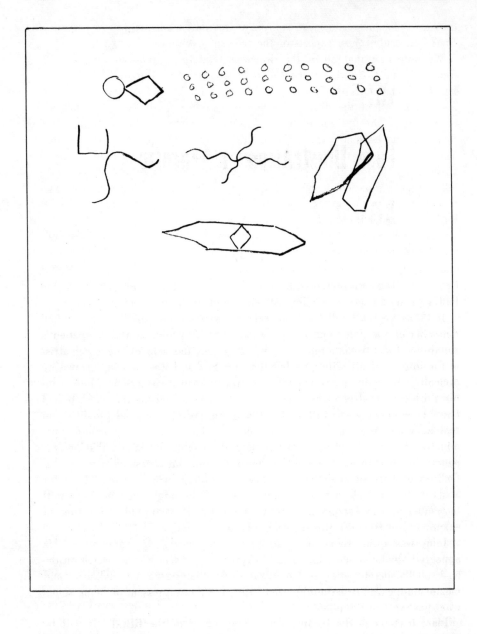

PLATE 6   A Neurotic Record (copy phase).

the basic phenomena in most cases and provide an adequate basis for inferences concerning most aspects of the relevant dynamics.

We note first that all of the drawings tend to be reduced in size, with figures A and 6 showing a marked reduction in size. Moreover, the spacing between some pairs of figures, notably A and 2, 4 and 6, and 6 and 7 is decreased. All of the drawings together occupy slightly less than one-half of the page. The position of figure A is not atypical, but, as we have noted, figure A, and especially the circle in this figure, is markedly reduced in size. The sequence is methodical; there is no collision or collision tendency; and there is no shift in the position of the test paper. These stylistic features tell us that this patient is generally orderly in his approach to new tasks and that he tends to be suppressive in his behavioral modes of expression. The initial reduction in size, the general reduction in use of space, and the reduction in size of figure 6 indicate, respectively, that he is fearful and anxious, that he tends to use repressive mechanisms of defense, and that he is especially anxious in emotionally toned situations. These stylistic features suggest that anal modes of adaptation are prominent in this individual's behavior and that, overtly, passivity may be a characteristic personality trait.

In the reproduction of figure A several features may be noted. The marked discrepancy in size between the circle and the square, the reduced size of the square, and the heavy line quality of the square suggest that this patient is attempting to identify unconsciously with a strong male role (as object preference) but that he feels inadequate in his male role. The presence of closure difficulty is indicative of anxiety in interpersonal situations, and this finding together with the relatively larger size of the square, the elongation of the square in the lateral dimension, the heavy line quality present in the square, and the irregularity in the line quality on the right, lower perimeter of the square suggest that there may be severe conflict in the sexual sphere and that the anxiety may be of the castration variety. More than this, the severity of the conflict as well as the jaggedness of the line referred to above may indicate some perverse tendencies, as well as the inappropriate fusing of sexual and aggressive drives. Finally, the possibility of some mild intracranial damage should not be overlooked (the difficulty with the angle of the square at the bottom).

We note, in figure 2, that there is a mild counterclockwise rotation of the entire figure. The columns of circles are so arranged that they form an arc of a circle (with the patient at the pivotal position). The narcissistic, oppositional features of the personality may be inferred from these two factors. Closure difficulty is again present. Another interesting feature is the gradual increase in size of the circles from left to right. This latter phenomenon suggests a tendency to act out, a tendency toward impulsivity in the personality which is otherwise fairly well concealed from overt observation.

The most striking feature of figure 4 is the closure difficulty (between curve and open square) and/or fragmentation of this Gestalt. The blocking in interpersonal situations has already been noted. The possibility that fragmentation is present reinforces the hypothesis of some mild organic damage. The inequality in the vertical sides of the open square again suggests the difficulty this man is having in maintaining an adequate self-percept in the role of a male, as well as the possibility of difficulty with authority figures. Some fine, poor incoordination is noted, further indication of the anxiety which is present. The curved portion of the figure is slightly exaggerated but the relative positions of the open square and curve are reproduced accurately. Perhaps the fragmentation enables this patient to handle this situation more easily than he could otherwise have done.

Figure 6 was presented in the same spatial orientation in which the patient reproduces it, i.e., no rotation is present. However, the figure is markedly reduced in size in both dimensions. The curves are drawn (especially the one in the horizontal plane) as a series of connected curves (and not as a smooth-flowing line). The amplitude of the curves is reduced and some "looping" occurs. The abient type of defense which this patient preferentially uses is made quite clear. He is unable to respond spontaneously in an emotional situation. He tries to control by repressive techniques; denial and isolation are suggested as defense mechanisms.

Figure 7 presents severe problems for this patient. The whole figure is rotated in a clockwise manner. Each part of the figure is modified slightly. Crossing difficulty is quite apparent as a consequence of the problem of overlapping. Sketching occurs even when the problem of overlapping is not present. Thus, although we must again suspect the presence of some intracranial damage, the depressive features of the reproduction and the sexually traumatic meaning of this stimulus seem much more prominent. These inferences are supported by the presence of line incoordination and the closure difficulties which can be noted in the response.

The same type of difficulties appear in figure 8, i.e., clockwise rotation, closure difficulty, and difficulty with the "phallic" endings of this Gestalt. Some mild line incoordination is also present. Moreover, the internal diamond is poorly drawn and shows repetitive line movements, suggesting conflict over the presence of this female symbol in an otherwise highly phallic figure. The phenomena which we have noted in common for both figures 7 and 8 suggest that the primary problem is one of psychosexual arrest and conflict. The over-all impression, reinforced by the findings on the last two figures, suggests the possibility of some type of sexual perversion as a residual of severe castration anxiety and some attempt at displacement of the locus of the anxiety.

Turning now to the elaborations (Plate 7), we note some striking similari-

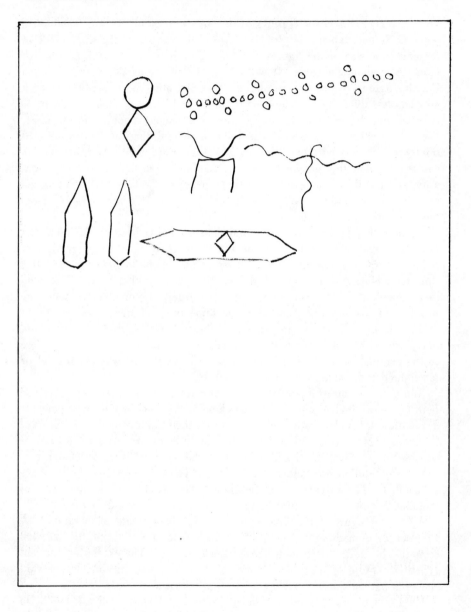

PLATE 7   A Neurotic Record (elaboration phase).

ties to the general stylistic features of the copy portion of the test. Methodical sequence is maintained, the drawings are compressed into the upper half of the page, the size of the figures (generally) is reduced, and the position of figure A is about the same. It will be noted that the curved portions of the Gestalt (figures A and 4) are placed *above* the other portions. The patient now has less difficulty with figure A than he had before (closure difficulty is reduced and the relative size of the two components is more appropriate). From these observations we can conclude, in general, that the most prominent inferences we derived from the *copy phase* are reinforced. Additionally, we can assume that this patient has strong feminine components in his personality, and possibly some exhibitionistic tendencies (the latter to be confirmed as plausible or rejected on the basis of additional evidence, possibly from the associations to the drawings).

We note that figure 2 is again rotated in a counterclockwise fashion, that poor line quality is evident on the open square portion of figure 4, that reduction of the amplitude of the curves again occurs on figure 6 (and this time mild clockwise rotation of the figure appears), that figure 7 is completely separated into two components (in order, presumably, to solve the problem of overlapping), and that the same types of difficulties present in figure 8 in the *copy phase* are present in the *elaboration phase*. Thus, again, our previous hypotheses are strengthened. These elaborations are very close to the original in basic Gestalt qualities, i.e., the patient was too fearful or too limited to be able to modify them freely.

And now, we can turn our attention to the associations which were obtained both to the original stimuli and to the elaborations. The patient first gave his association to his elaboration of figure A and then to the stimulus, as follows: "An ornament. A ring with a do-dunny. Could be an ornament for a bracelet or something," and: "Ball and a block." The association to the elaboration suggests exhibitionistic fantasies. The verbal blocking indicates the presence of conflict. The orientation is feminine. The association to the original stimulus is quite concrete and literal. Fantasy is limited and guarded.

Again, on figure 2 the first association is given to the elaboration: "A bracelet or something to me." When asked to associate to the original stimulus, he said: "Both look like bracelets to me." The exhibitionistic and repetitive nature of these associations should be noted. It can also be said that this patient's speech style contains egocentric features.

He associated to the elaboration of figure 4: "A stand and a basin." He could give no association to the stimulus. The possible superego characteristics of his association (which may be inferred from the need to wash oneself) should not be overlooked. The block in associating to the original figure is indicative of the presence of anxiety, which tends to confirm our speculations concerning his difficulties in copying this figure. It should also be noted that his association tends to deny the higher (superior) position of the basin (one wonders why he did not say, "A basin on a stand").

He associated only to the elaboration of figure 6. He said: "A piece of string. Might be a kind of wire—a crooked wire." This association appears to be evasive. The "crooked wire" may be a reference to his self-percept, i.e., distorted or bent.

On figure 7, he responded, again, to the elaboration: "I don't know. Some kind of ornament or something. Something like the top of a picket fence." Again, the exhibitionistic needs of this patient become apparent. The fence may connote the need for protection while the picket-type of fence suggests many possibilities among which the phallic connotation is the most parsimonious in terms of other evidence already obtained for this figure. He could give no association to the original stimulus.

His only association to figure 8 was to the original stimulus. His association: "Some kind of a sign. They have on fences." The continued association to "fence" suggests a perseverative trend in his thinking as well as the probable need for protection, suggested before. The association "sign" is often related to feelings of guilt and suspiciousness.

Taking into account all of the data from the three phases of the RBGT, we are able to present the following summary of our analysis. This man appears to be a fairly dependent and very anxious individual. He shows considerable concern about maintaining a conventional "facade" and tends to be conforming and compliant in his behavior. There is some rigidity in his behavior. Ego controls are reasonably well maintained except for problems involving specific sexual traumata. Affective behavior is reduced and spontaneity is lacking. He has considerable doubt concerning his adequacy as a person. Superego functions are fairly strict but are insufficient to prevent occasional break-through of libidinal impulses.

Although this man is essentially conforming in his behavior, the severity of his conflicts and the possible impairment which intracranial damage has caused, produce some overt types of psychopathology. His strong oral-dependent needs and his internal tension are consistent with his use of alcohol. The narcissistic and oral features of the personality as well as the anal components which are present suggest that he has strong exhibitionistic needs and may engage in some other perverse sexual behavior. In turn, the use of alcohol and the predicted perversions, together with his superego formation, will produce considerable guilt and tension. His feelings of impotence and his sexual-aggressive drives may result in both homosexual needs and practices. Some form of perversion as a displacement of his castration anxiety may also be present.

The basic features of the personality are psychoneurotic in character and the primary features of the defense system are obsessive-compulsive, with denial and isolation, as part of a general repressive orientation, high in the defense hierarchy. The presence of some mild intracranial damage, possibly a small tumor, is suspected and may account for the apparent, expressive aphasia and for the reduced effectiveness of ego controls.

It is suggested that this man will be. willing to accept psychotherapy if, in fact, his conflicts are as severe as is suspected and he is confronted with them. However, psychotherapy may be expected to be long and difficult. Some reduction in the severity of the superego may be anticipated, some release of anxiety may be accomplished, and more effective ways of sublimating his oedipal problems, and especially his oral and anal needs, may be secured. Careful neurologic examination is also suggested to evaluate the possibility of brain damage.

Subsequent psychiatric and neurologic examination, and subsequent psychotherapeutic intervention revealed the following. Unknown to the wife, this man had been engaging in homosexual practices for almost the entire period of his marriage. So far as could be learned, he had shown no overt homosexuality previously. He described, in his therapeutic sessions, two experiences in which he had exhibited himself before adolescent girls. On one occasion he had had sexual relations with a 12 year old girl, and he had described to the psychiatrist his obsessive concern with smelling and fondling this girl's genitalia. He discussed his strong urges to engage in perverse sexual practices as well as his strong conflicts in this regard. The neurologist reported that this man suffered from a small parietotemporal tumor for which operative care was not indicated. He did receive concurrent psychotherapeutic and general medical care. The therapist reported that this patient was able to make moderate gains in reducing guilt and anxiety, that he was able to function better on his job, and that there was some improvement, but not complete cessation, in his alcoholism. He had developed a hobby involving sculpturing with clay materials which was very satisfying to him. He left therapy after 72 sessions, spaced over a year and a half, because he felt he was able to get along fairly well and the financial drain was more than he could tolerate.

IX

Case Illustration: A Character Problem

This chapter is concerned with the analysis of an RBGT record produced by a patient whose diagnosis is a character disorder. Detailed interpretation of all three phases of the basic method of administration will be presented, as well as relevant case history material, other psychological test data, and a summary from psychotherapeutic data.

The patient was a 28 year old white female. She was a high school graduate and had had approximately one year of college. She had never held a full-time job.

The drawings were made with the right hand in a rapid manner. If counting took place, it was done silently and imperceptibly. The stimulus cards utilized were the American Orthopsychiatric Association version.

In the *copy phase* (Plates 8 and 9), we note that the drawings are distributed over two pages in an irregular sequence. There are five deviations: figure A to 1, 1 to 2, 2 to 3, 3 to 4, 4 to 5. In general, the figures are increased in size, though the spacing is irregular, varying from constricted through adequate to excessive.

The initial impression is that of an outgoing, aggressively oriented woman (size, two sheets of paper) who is markedly conflicted over the expression of hostility (varied spacing). Impulses are poorly controlled and ego functions are uneven (irregular sequence). A second order hypothesis is that tension is externalized, and as tension becomes pronounced, considerable impulsive acting-out can be expected.

The initial progression of the sequence is atypical. After placing figure A almost in the center of the page, the patient placed figure 1 *above* it, proceeded downward for figure 2, but then moved from the bottom of the page toward the top of the page for figures 3 and 4. Only after running out of space does she regain a more usual sequence by moving downward

115

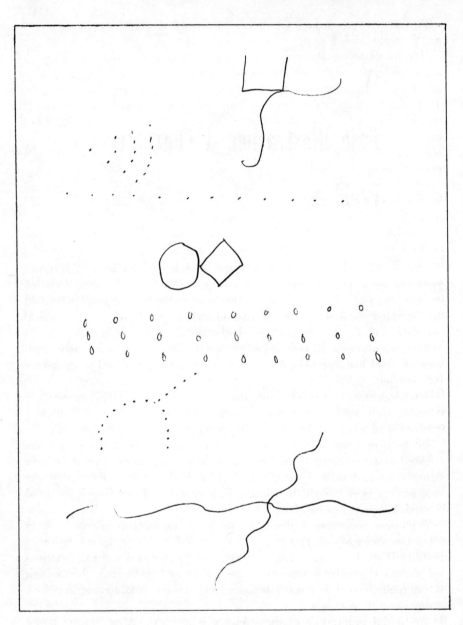

PLATE 8   A Character Problem (copy phase).

with figures 5 and 6 and continuing in an orderly fashion with figures 7 and 8 on the second page.

Her initial atypical sequence from figure A to figure 1 suggests oppositional tendencies as well as difficulties with authority figures. The hypothesis advanced is that she reacts to such figures with negativism and resentment. That these feelings are at least preconscious is suggested by her regaining control with figure 2, but the strength of these feelings is again evidenced by her treatment of the next two figures. Conformity is helped by circumstances (the patient "ran out" of space), and with this external aid, she regains control and conforms for the remainder of the copy phase.

Inferences: Immaturity and infantile rebellious attitudes at a preconscious level with strong covert dependent needs. Consequently, ambivalence toward strong, authoritarian figures is indicated.

Turning to the individual figures, we note that figure A is placed almost in the center of the page and is reduced in size over-all. Closure difficulty is evident in the joining of both parts of the figure as well as in the circle and the square. Both the circle and the square are drawn in an irregular manner with fairly heavy pencil pressure. Compared to the square, the circle is slightly enlarged.

Despite anxiety (pencil pressure, reduction in size), the patient nevertheless reacts in an impulsive, egocentric and narcissistic manner (placement of figure). An inadequate attempt at identification with the mother is suggested (enlarged circle, irregularity) and fearful and conflicted attitudes toward the father are also indicated (decreased square, irregularity). Oedipal difficulty is likely. Inability to establish enduring relationships with the parents and consequent difficulty in maintaining enduring cathexes with people is an additional finding (closure difficulty).

Figure 1 is reproduced with the correct number of dots. It is mildly rotated in a clockwise direction and is increased in its lateral dimension. Depressive tendencies are suggested, and the increased size indicates difficulty in interpersonal relations, with the additional implication that she feels the need to relate to satisfy covert dependency. (Conversely, decreased lateral size would be related to fearfulness in interpersonal relationships and consequent withdrawal).

The manner in which the dots are executed is interesting. The first four are adequate but they then become dashes (retrogression); this appears to be the result of impulsivity and possible regression under tension. Note that the movement from figure A to figure 1 is upward as previously described; the underlying conflict with authority apparently produces anxiety and depression as the derivatives of her oppositional tendencies. Her impulsivity and readiness to externalize her own feelings indicates unwillingness to accept

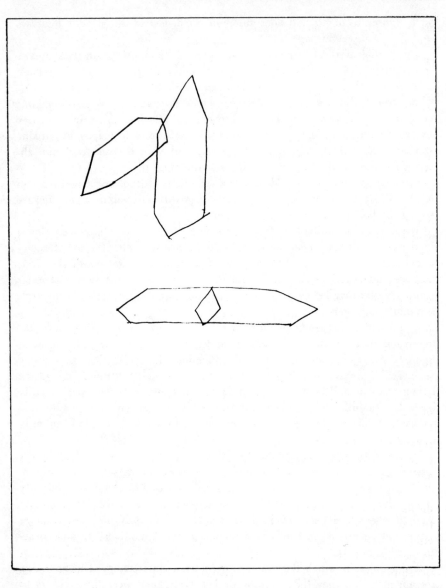

PLATE 9   A Character Problem continued (copy phase).

responsibility for behavior which, in the extreme, could lead to paranoid-like tendencies. However, in light of the apparent immaturity of this patient, such paranoid-like behavior is closer to the behavior of the child who, when confronted with an empty cookie jar rationalizes by blaming his toy bear.

Figure 2 is increased in its lateral dimension. The circles vary to loops and ovals and the number of columns is reduced to nine. While the angulation is preserved, the upper line of circles is mildly rotated in a counterclockwise manner and the lower line of dots is mildly rotated in a clockwise direction; thus the Gestalt is gradually and successively increased, from left to right, in its vertical dimension.

Impulsive tendencies are pronounced (treatment of circles, incorrect number of columns). Both opposition and depressive elements are present (rotation) and difficulty in relating to people is apparent, with confirmed evidence that she tends to form dependent relationships which she then is unable to accept (increased lateral size).

Proceeding to figure 3, we note that the dots are impulsively drawn, being transformed into dashes (retrogression). The figure is mildly rotated in a clockwise direction and the figure is reduced in its lateral dimension.

Confirmation of this patient's depressive tendencies as well as impulsivity is indicated by the rotation and retrogressions. However, the reduction of the figure's lateral size is inconsistent with the previous figure being increased in this dimension. While this change in lateral size confirms the previous hypothesis of difficulty with interpersonal relationships, tendencies toward withdrawal are now also suggested. Perhaps the symbolically hostile values of figure 3 precipitated the patient's reaction. We would then hypothesize that although she usually aggressively seeks dependent relationships, perceived hostility results in her rapid withdrawal with associated depressive feelings. Analysis of the patient's modifications and associations may provide additional clues.

Closure difficulty is evident in figure 4. The tangential curved portion is displaced under the open square and is also increased in size. The patient's treatment of this portion of the Gestalt is similar to her performance on the circle in figure A and confirms her inadequate feminine identification as well as persistent inability to establish and maintain mature interpersonal relationships. Impulsivity is again indicated by the manner in which the curved portion was drawn, rapidly sweeping from right to left with increasing pencil pressure and ending in an additional loop. Considerable tension is suggested by the very fine tremulousness that appears in the upper right hand portion of the curve. In examining the open square we also find that while the vertical lines are of approximate equal length, they both slant to the right, and the horizontal line joining them is irregularly drawn. Again, confirmation of the finding on figure A appears: conflicted attitudes toward the father.

Again in figure 5 we find the circular portion slightly increased in size, with an accompanying reduction in the number of dots in the secant (five instead of seven). Impulsivity and tension are evident in the quality of dots and in the irregularity of the circular portion in its lower left extremity. Hypothesis: further support for this patient's difficulty with feminine identification and her conflicted attitudes toward males.

Figure 6 is markedly increased in size in both its dimensions. The curves are both skewed and reduced in amplitude. Pencil pressure increases as the horizontal line is completed. Inferences: Expansive, aggressive behavior can be expected under the impact of emotionally laden stimuli. Emotional lability is present and attempts at control to prevent over-reaction are only partially successful.

Figure 7 is increased in size, particularly the right hexagon. Closure difficulty is evident in the lower corners of the right hexagon, angulation difficulty also appears, and the point of junction between each element of the figure is displaced to the right. The phallic characteristics of this Gestalt and the patient's adient reaction to them points up her oedipal conflicts and her consequent identification with the father toward whom her attitudes are markedly conflicted. Emotional lability is further suggested by the angulation changes.

Figure 8 repeats the findings in figure 7: increased size, angulation and closure difficulties. This lends support to the hypothesis developed above, and the proportionately increased size of the internal diamond further supports the inference of an attempted masculine identification.

Turning our attention to the patient's elaborations and associations, we note that the drawings are distributed on one page in a methodical sequence. In general, size and use of space are adequate. Furthermore, though the patient does make modifications, each Gestalt is recognizable and she returns all of the original elements to her reproductions. That is, dots remain dots, circles remain circles and so on. Consequently, she continues the sequence begun on figure 5 in the *copy phase* discussed above. This suggests that her initial reaction is characteristically impulsive and labile, she nevertheless has the capacity for control as she becomes more familiar with the demands of the situation. Ego resources are therefore good.

Figure A is modified so that the square encompasses the circle. Her comment is that this "looks better." The patient's treatment of this figure points up her attempt at a masculine indentification along with denying femininity.

Figure 1 is transformed into an angular shape, the number of dots is reduced and the patient associates a "hatchet" to her production. Considerable latent hostility is suggested, as well as emotional lability, by her transformation of

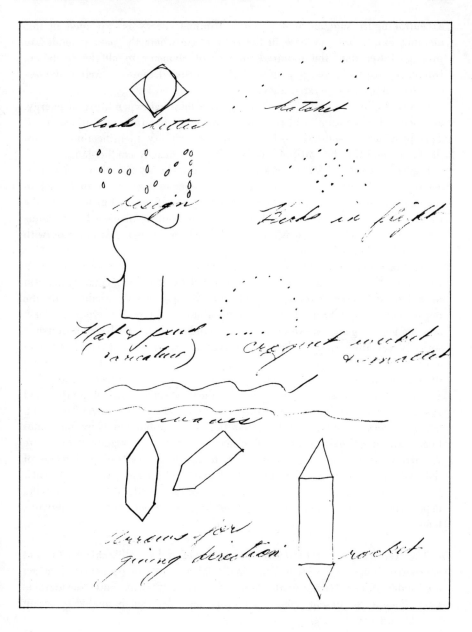

PLATE 10 A Character Problem (elaborations).

a neutral figure into an angular one. Minimal energy is expended in this modification, as was the case in the *copy phase* where the patient tended to produce fewer than the required number of elements in all the Gestalten. Inference: available energy is limited by repressive defenses as well as depressive tendencies, as suggested above.

Figure 2 offers several leads. It suggests a minimal expenditure of energy, as discussed above, but is also a mirror image of her father's initials, N. H. This provides substantial evidence that her primary identification is with the father and that her attitudes toward him are heavily conflict-laden.

Figure 3 is rotated 90 degrees in a counterclockwise direction and is perceived as a flight of birds. Withdrawal tendencies previously suggested in the analysis of the *copy phase* of this figure are confirmed. Furthermore, the rotation suggests the oppositional tendencies previously discussed and points up the lability of the patient's potential reactions in her relationships with perceived authority figures.

Moving rapidly through the remaining modifications and associations, confirmation of narcissistic elements is suggested by the ornamental symbolism of a hat and purse (figure 4). The phallic and hostile qualities of the personality are emphasized by the associations to figure 5: "croquet wicket and mallet," a game in which a female symbol (ball) is driven through a series of female sexual symbols (wickets) to make contact (identify?) with a phallic symbol (poles). We might speculate upon the potential oedipal drama of this association in which the patient (ball) conquers the mother (wickets) to possess the father (pole). Further suggestions of phallic and castrating elements in the personality are indicated by the association to figure 8 of "rocket," along with the separation of the pointed ends by horizontal lines. Additional evidence of phallic dependency is also suggested by figure 7, "arrows" for giving directions. With regard to the castrating elements of the patient's personality, note the cut-off end of the right "arrow." Finally, figure 6 (association: "waves") suggest orality with its accompanying dependency. This association is also suggestive of possible addictive tendencies.

The test results are, therefore, indicative of a basically narcissistic and egocentric individual who is emotionally labile and can be expected to act out under minimal emotional stress. She is aggressive, and considerable latent hostility is present. She is markedly dependent but is unable to accept this dependency.

The basic conflict appears to be oedipal in nature. The patient has made a paternal identification and at the same time has strongly ambivalent attitudes toward her father. Her identification with the mother is partial and incomplete. Consequently, confusion over her sexual identity is evident and she denies her feminine wishes while attempting to assume a masculine role. Conflict with the father and other perceived strong males results and she reacts with oppositional tendencies and negativism. Overtly she is demanding, infantile and suspicious, acting out freely and externalizing the basis for her own behavior.

Secondary paranoid reactions are thus likely. She is likely to become anxious easily, react with depression and possible addiction to alcohol and/or drugs, particularly as these would enable her to become more dependent.

Ego functioning, though occasionally uneven, is nevertheless intact. No evidence of psychotic functioning appears in the RBGT record. All Gestalten are adequately perceived and reproduced and no primary psychotic manifestations are present.

The patient's basic modes of adaptation described above appear to be a fundamental and characteristic part of her personality. Her apparent inability to be aware of and modify them suggests that they are ego-syntonic or characterologic in nature rather than classically psychoneurotic. The lability, impulsivity, and oedipal nature of her problem further suggests that this is an hysterical character disorder.

As this patient's history is reconstructed, we find that she very early perceived her mother as a weak, ineffectual woman dominated by her husband, and consequently the patient gave her up as a source of identification. On the other hand, she idolized her father who was perceived as a very intelligent, rigid, moralistic person, and she expressed positive feelings regarding him. He was very affectionate to her when she was a child, but when she was eight years old, her father told her that she was too big to sit on his lap and this made her feel rejected by him. At the same time he also indicated that she was too big to "spank in the regular place" and subsequently punished her by slapping her hands.

After her eighth year, rebellious attitudes toward the father began to develop and she was unable to accept his continual "interference" in her life. Their relationship became so bad that they no longer spoke, but communicated with each other in writing.

She maintained few close interpersonal relationships outside of her home during adolescence and dated very little because of her father's strict demands and interference.

However, away at college, she met a law student and was married, giving up further education to help support him as he continued school. She looked to her marriage as a situation which would bolster her security and unconsciously gratify her dependency wishes. But since her husband was not strong or consistent enough in his own orientation and had marked dependent problems of his own, her conflicts were intensified rather than reduced.

Following the marriage, a series of traumata served to reactivate still further her old conflicts concerning her inadequacy and guilt. She learned to enjoy sexual relations but the birth of her children made her feel trapped, and a congenital heart defect of one of them caused guilt and dependency needs to emerge. Then, separation from her husband due to his military service, her inability to find gratification in an occupation, and her inadequate sublimation in her domestic life reactivated and reinforced old problems. Regression and acting-out became means of defending against severe conflicts, and the use of drugs and alcohol offered temporary respite but increased her marital problems.

When initially seen for psychological consultation, the patient appeared clinically to be anxious and mildly depressed. She was consulting several physicians and had obtained copious supplies of amphetamines, barbiturates and ataraxics. She was also consuming approximately a pint of whiskey each day. Despite heavy medication, she was unable to sleep at night, and though taking liberal doses of amphetamine during the day, was fatigued and unable to do any housework. She insisted on and was able to obtain a full-time maid. Her appearance was poor; she dressed in sweaters and skirts or knit dresses, often wearing the same outfit for days at a time. Little or no makeup was used.

The patient was seen therapeutically for a period of two years. She rapidly formed a positive transference and a highly dependent relationship with the therapist. Her presenting symptoms of anxiety and depression soon remitted, but she externalized and projected the basis of her difficulties upon her husband. She refused to take responsibility for her behavior, acted out impulsively and rationalized her behavior as being the only possible reaction to her impossible situation. Basically unsure of herself and unable to accept the permissive and understanding therapist's interest in her, especially as she became aware of her dependency, she began to test and provoke him, coming forty-five minutes late for appointments and then expecting a full session, missing sessions completely, and calling him at 3 or 4 a.m. to discuss trivial matters which she insisted were emergencies. She made other excessive demands and would react with petulance and negativism when they were not met. When confronted with her inconsistencies, she would respond with anger and bewilderment.

Though she insisted she could not continue in various, difficult situations, when she was unable to enlist outside aid, she not only functioned but did so in a most adequate manner. As therapy progressed she began to differentiate herself and become aware of and deal more effectively with her reality problems, functioning in a more realistic, independent manner. Her intake of drugs and alcohol diminished and was finally eliminated. However, before therapy could be completed, circumstances caused her to move out of the area and the therapeutic relationship was terminated.

The characterologic nature of this woman's problems is pointed up by the history and therapeutic data. Other psychological test results were supportive of her narcissistic orientation, emotional lability, covert dependency and over-all hysterical orientation indicated by the analysis of the RBGT protocol.

X

Case Illustration: An Organic Problem

In this chapter we shall present the RBGT record of a patient with an organic problem. Only the *copy phase* of the basic method of administration was employed. The record (Plate 11) will be analyzed in terms of the principles discussed in Chapters V and VI in order to illustrate the interaction of psychological and organic factors in the production of the test protocol. Following this, a brief clinical summary will be presented.

The patient is a 62 year old Negro male. His educational history included completion of the tenth grade. His occupational history included work as a cook and unskilled labor preparing skins for cold storage.

He cooperated fully in the psychological examination. On the RBGT all of the figures were drawn with the right hand. The drawings were made in a careful manner and were done very slowly.

An initial, over-all inspection of the record reveals that the patient has utilized one sheet of paper and arranged the figures in an irregular sequence. (The first change in sequence occurs following figure 3, when he shifts from a vertical to a lateral progression in his placement. Figure 6 presents the second shift in sequence, and figures 7 and 8 indicate additional shifts.) The spacing of the figures is unusual: figures A, 1 and 2 are grouped, with a normal amount of space between them; figure 3 is isolated, and separated from figure 2 by an unusually large amount of space; and the remaining five figures are compressed into less than one-quarter of the page. Furthermore, there is a collision between figures 5 and 8, and collision tendencies involve figures 2, 4, and 6.

The sequential arrangement, spacing, collision and collision tendencies indicate poor planning and inadequate judgment, suggesting the initial hypothesis of impaired ego functioning. Since the drawings were done slowly, we infer impulsivity was not a factor and that the patient was, in fact,

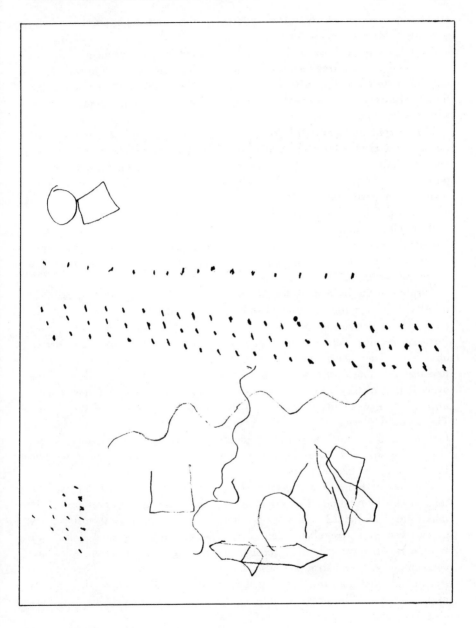

PLATE 11   An Organic Record.

attempting to overcontrol. The failure of these attempts points up the severity of his ego impairment.

A tendency toward use of the margin is evident in the placement of figures A, 1, 2 and 3, suggesting feelings of insecurity, or inadequacy, and compensatory attempts in dealing with these feelings. The cohesion of the remaining figures also reflects withdrawal tendencies and passivity as an attempt to cope with tension and perceived inadequacies.

The over-all line quality of the drawings manifests poor coordination, particularly the dots, which are quite heavy and irregular. These factors support the impression of compensatory attempts at control on the part of the patient and further suggest that considerable tension and/or neurologic involvement is present.

At this point, the evidence taken together tentatively suggests that we are dealing with an individual whose ego functions are markedly disturbed, who has strong feelings of inadequacy, is anxious, reacts with passivity and withdrawal and is making strong compensatory attempts at restitution which are relatively unsuccessful.

Turning to the individual designs, figure A is placed in a slightly atypical position. Though the essential Gestalt is preserved, closure difficulty is evident in both the closing of the circle and the joining of circle and square; furthermore, the vertical and horizontal axes of the square are drawn obliquely. The "gaps" in closure suggest difficulty in maintaining interpersonal relationships, characterized by withdrawal, but, in the light of the over-all line quality which is discussed above, may also reflect motor incoordination, a possibility supported by the lopsided appearance of the square. The atypical placement of figure A supports the hypotheses of an ego disturbance and of fearfulness in interpersonal relations. The relatively larger size of the square in relation to the circle suggests an unconscious need to identify with the masculine role.

The dots of figure 1 are positioned in a wavering line with an over-all, mild clockwise rotation. Perseveration B is indicated by the presence of 16 dots instead of the 12 called for by the stimulus. The dots themselves are overworked and irregular. Depressive features are suggested (clockwise rotation). Attempts at binding tension through the use of internalization and compensatory overcontrol are also supported (dot quality). Loss of ego functioning continues to be indicated (perseveration B and wavering quality of the Gesalt). The heavy quality of the dots indicates that compensatory efforts to maintain control are being made.

The same general factors observed in figure 1 are present in figure 2 with the addition of perseveration A. These perseverative factors introduce the hypothesis of rather severe rigidity in this patient. In addition, the substitution of dots for circles in this figure is indicative of retrogression on a relatively simple task, suggesting the possibility of diffuse brain damage.

The excessive spacing between figures 2 and 3 with the subsequent placement of figure 3 in the lower left-hand corner of the page would appear to be a result of the patient's attempt to better orient his drawings by using the corner as a guide. However, the increased use of space suggests that hostile impulses are present and tend to find occasional expression. The patient's sequential reaction to this outburst is apparently reflected in the compression of the figure by decreasing its horizontal dimension. This points up his persistent attempts at adjustment through withdrawal. Angulation is decreased, indicating overcontrol and underreaction to emotional stimuli and/or possible neurologic deficit. Dot quality is consistent in figures 1 and 2 and supports the hypothesis that the patient uses internalization and attempts to overcontrol.

The line quality of figure 4 is tremulous, with evidence of poor coordination and poor control in the "overshooting" at the top of the curved portion of the Gestalt and the top of the right vertical line of the open square. The hostility indicated by the excessive space between figures 2 and 3 now appears to be related to conflict with authority figures (increased length of the right vertical in the open square). The hypothesis is that this patient has strong hostile impulses which are related to basic conflict with authority figures. In general, this patient does not express hostility directly but, rather, suppresses it, as suggested by the persistent tendencies toward withdrawal and by overcontrol and internalization indicated by the data thus far. However, his impaired ego functioning interferes with these defenses to the extent that occasional loss of control occurs, with subsequent expression of hostility. Closure difficulty is also present, as it was in figure A. Difficulty in interpersonal relationships characterized by withdrawal as hypothesized above now seems to be supported. However, since the closure difficulty is accompanied by incoordination, by poor over-all line quality in all the figures, and by "overshooting" on the curved portion of the Gestalt, the hypothesis of brain damage is further supported.

Simplification of figure 5 points up the patient's impotence and inadequacy in dealing with a relatively complex stimulus. Here again, tremulous line quality suggests motor incoordination on a neurologic basis. The irregular and uneven quality of the curved portion of this figure, the slight counterclockwise rotation, and the severe reduction in size of the figure support not only the hypothesis of diffuse organic damage but also reinforce the impression of a basically passive reaction to unconscious hostile wishes.

Figure 6 is increased in size, particularly in the lateral dimension. There is some irregularity of the curves, with considerable flattening of the vertical curve. The intersecting angle is more nearly square than acute and the entire figure is mildly rotated in a counterclockwise direction. The collision tendencies noted above are present. Hypotheses: loss of control under emotional stimulation is pronounced; with such loss of control, hostile impulses gain expression; conflict with authority figures, as previously suggested, is evident; and a mild tension state with accompanying motor incoordination is indicated.

Overlapping difficulty, simplification, and closure difficulty are apparent in figure 7. This Gestalt is drawn as one continuous figure rather than as two overlapping hexagons. The line quality is irregular and changes in pencil pressure as indicated by dark and light lines are evident. The patient also spent more time on this figure than any other in the test. For the first time in the test series the essential Gestalt is lost, though it is also evident that the patient tried very hard to preserve it. The patient's performance on this figure points up his inability to deal with a relatively complex stimulus. In spite of this, he persists in his attempt to solve the problem, at the same time revealing his impotence. Compensatory controls are re-established. The marked evidence of closure difficulty indicates that a frustrating task leads to increased irritability and other difficulties in interpersonal relations. An additional hypothesis is that of sexual impotency.

Figure 8 is slightly reduced in the horizontal dimension. The internal diamond is moved to the left of center and is increased in size so that it extends below the bottom of the lower boundary of the hexagon. In sharp contrast to figure 7, the hexagon form is adequately reproduced, though the patient had difficulty with the left "point." Closure difficulty and incoordination are again manifest. Collision with figure 5 is evident. Impaired ego functioning and inability to plan adequately are indicated. Feelings of impotence (treatment of points) and compensatory attempts at a masculine identification (increased size of diamond) are suggested along with his tendency toward withdrawal (decreased horizontal dimension).

This record is striking in the consistency of factors in it which suggest rather severe impairment of ego functions. There are several clinical syndromes which could produce such impairment.

Mental deficiency can be ruled out on the basis of the maturity of the patient's reproduction of the Gestalten, particularly figure 8 and his attempt at figure 7 as a continuous line, which suggests his previous functioning at a better than average intellectual level. Furthermore, the mental defective characteristically simplifies Gestalten by separating the figures into their essential elements.

Such impairment of ego functioning may occur in instances of acute, though transitory, anxiety reactions. Though it is evident that tension is reflected in this record, the anxiety is not severe, and slow, methodical methods of work are not consistent with such a reaction.

Consequently, the problem posed at this point is the differential diagnosis between psychosis, functional or organic, and organic brain damage.

There is little evidence of regression in the protocol, and though deficiency in ego functioning is present, reality testing appears adequate. Only one of the Gestalten is inadequately reproduced, and even in this case, the relationship between the elements of the figure is preserved. Rather, the specific ego deficiency appears to be related to poor judgment and planning ability. Furthermore, despite ample evidence of incoordination, the patient appears to be manifesting a perceptual difficulty rather than difficulty in execution. The adequate hexagon drawn in figure eight suggests that the difficulty with figure 7 resulted from an inability to organize the Gestalt perceptually rather than from inability to reproduce the hexagonal figures. This marked difficulty in perceptual organization of a relatively complex stimulus is suggestive of diffuse intracranial pathology rather than psychosis.

The evidence of impotence, rigidity and compensatory attempts at control in this RBGT record are personality factors also associated with organic brain damage.

At this point, it is evident that the patient is a brain-damaged individual who is mildly depressed and anxious, feels impotent and has apparently reacted with rigidity and compensatory mechanisms to attempt to maintain his adjustment. What, then, can be said of his premorbid personality?

The primary personality appears to be that of an individual who has difficulty in establishing enduring interpersonal cathexes, utilizes passive mechanisms and tends to withdraw rather than act in an aggressive manner. Tension is dealt with by internalization. A basic area of conflict appears to be associated with authority figures, and the resulting hostility is repressed. Under the impact of emotionally laden situations, some loss of control occurs, with accompanying tendencies toward impulsivity.

As a result of the brain damage, several major factors appear. There is an intensification of his feelings of impotence and an exaggeration of his previous attempts at adjustment through the use of suppressive techniques. The patient's attempts at compensatory control, so evident in the test data, are a consequence of this. But his defenses, though intensified, are less effective and he also tends to lose control more easily.

Approximately 18 months prior to testing, the patient became aware of a sudden weakness of his left arm and leg, causing him to fall to the ground. Initially, there was some slight improvement so that he was able to walk into his home. However, the following morning there was complete paralysis of the left side of his body. Upon hospitalization, the medical findings included bloody spinal fluid. Recovery was good so that at the time of the psychological evaluation, there was only slight residual weakness of the left extremities. The patient walked with a slight limp and had good use of his left arm and hand.

A recent medical examination disclosed weakness of the left arm and leg, slightly accentuated deep tendon reflexes on the left, positive Hoffman, positive Babinski on the left, a sustained clonus in the left ankle, and a slight loss of tactile sensation on the left side. Ophthalmic examination revealed bilateral arcus senilis, tortuosity of the fundi, silver streaking of the arterioles and minimal arteriovenous compression. The final impression was cerebral arteriosclerosis and residua of a left hemiplegia resulting from a mild cerebral vascular accident.

Clinically, the patient appeared neatly dressed and well-groomed. He spoke coherently using good vocabulary. His conversation during casual interaction seemed adequate; however, when relatively complex instructions were given him, he was unable to understand them fully and act accordingly.

The patient arrived for his appointment two hours late explaining that he was unable to find the building. However, evidence from the nursing home at which he resides indicates that he is forgetful. In this connection he insisted that his stroke took place in 1957 despite hospital records which indicated its occurrence in 1958.

Additional clinical findings include a Wechsler Bellevue IQ of 78 with component IQ's of 87 verbally and 70 on the performance scale. There was evidence of concrete thinking, poor memory, and inability to organize and synthesize. On the block design subtest, he also confused the yellow with the white colors. The overall impression derived from the patient's performance on the Wechsler Bellevue was that of organic brain damage.

Consequently, the medical evidence as well as the additional psychological evidence supports the impression of this patient derived from his performance on the RBGT; namely, diffuse intracranial damage.

XI

Case Illustration: A Case of Mental Retardation

Presented in this chapter is the *copy phase* of the RBGT record produced by a patient who is a primary mental defective. The record (Plate 12) will be analyzed in the manner utilized in preceding chapters.

The patient is a 25 year old Caucasian female. After failing to complete the second grade, she was placed in special education classes until the school authorities dismissed her as "unable to learn." She has never held a job.

She was fully cooperative during the testing and used her right hand in drawing all the figures. She worked slowly and carefully, taking a longer than average amount of time to complete her drawings. Her comments during the testing were: "I can't do it," "I don't know," "It's confusing."

Initial inspection of the record indicates that the patient has arranged her drawings on one sheet of paper in a methodical sequence (only two changes in direction occur: between figures 5 and 6, 7 and 8). All the figures are placed in the upper half of the page, and are generally appropriate in size but over-all use of space is constricted.

These factors suggest that the patient's ego functions are adequate (sequence and size) but that the general orientation is passive and characterized by withdrawal. Such hostile impulses as may occur are repressed (constricted use of space).

Line quality is relatively uniform, with little evidence of incoordination. The lines are drawn firmly with good pressure, suggesting that impulses are usually well-controlled.

Figure A is placed in a usual locus. It is drawn as a separate circle and square with considerable space between the two elements of the figure. No effort is apparently made by the patient to bring these elements together. For this reason, closure difficulty is not scored; rather, the drawing manifests fragmentation or simplification, and the question is raised as to whether this

133

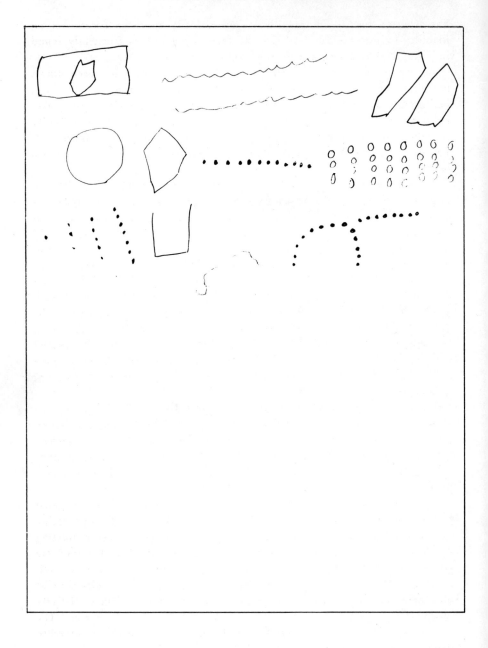

PLATE 12 A Mental Defective Record.

has occurred because of inability to execute the figure or because of an inability to perceive the total Gestalt. Such separation is frequently found in young children, mental defectives, schizophrenics and organics.

In examining figure A in detail, we note that the circle has been drawn by joining two segments in a well-articulated manner. The patient, however, had great difficulty with the obverted square, finally producing it as a five-sided figure. Inference: perceptual, coordinational or maturational difficulty in which an earlier level (circle: 3 year) is unaffected but a higher level (obverted square: 7 year) has either not been attained or regression has occurred.

The correct number of dots has been reproduced in figure 1. The dots are heavily filled in, suggesting considerable investment of energy in a relatively simple task. Hypothesis: tension is bound through internalization and compulsive ritual. There is a decrease in the lateral dimension of this figure, and it is mildly rotated in a clockwise direction, suggesting difficulty and withdrawal as an interpersonal technique and possible depressive tendencies.

Figure 2 is also decreased in its lateral dimension, is reproduced with an inadequate number of columns (8 instead of 10), but is composed of well-articulated circles. The reduction in the number of columns appears to be due to poor planning or anticipatory ability in that the design is ended when it reaches the edge of the paper. The angulation of the columns is changed to the vertical. The first column is correctly composed of a series of three circles but subsequent columns consist of series of four circles, a form of perseveration B.

The patient's adequate reproduction of the circles of this figure suggests capable functioning at a lower maturational level. The angulation difficulty may indicate underaction to emotional stimuli (decreased acuity of angles) but also suggests maturational or organic involvement. Withdrawal in interpersonal relations is also further supported (decreased lateral dimensions). Rigidity is also indicated (perseveration B).

The patient manifests angulation difficulty on figure 3. The angulated lines of dots are drawn straight, with the angulation approximated by rotating each line of dots in a counterclockwise direction, without, however, rotating the figure itself. Consequently, the patient maintains a semblance of the angulation in this figure, but is unable to angulate each line about its midpoint. The basic Gestalt is lost; however, this can also be considered to be a form of simplification and it suggests difficulty in coping with a relatively complex stimulus as well as maturational and/or organic components. The dots in this figure are heavily worked over, supporting the previous inference that the patient internalizes tension.

Turning to figure 4, we find that the patient has again separated the Gestalt into its two separate elements. The open square is well retained, except that the right vertical is somewhat longer than the left vertical. Hypothesis: conflict with authority, suppression of hostility and a probable passive orientation to authority figures (sequence and organization, overworking of dots). The patient has great difficulty with the curved portion of figure 4. The curve is slightly irregular, is flattened and an additional tiny loop appears in the lower left-hand corner. Inferences: difficulty in rhythmic coordination involving complex curved forms, suggesting a maturational deficit and a tendency to underreact to emotional stimuli. The fragmentation and simplification of figure 4 also support the hypothesis that this is a maturational, organic or psychotic problem.

Figure 5 is well drawn with the exception of a moderate clockwise rotation of the slanting portion. The dot quality is consistent with that previously described. The hypothesis that this patient deals with tension by internalization and controls impulses adequately is supported. The excellent quality of the curved portion of this Gestalt indicates that the patient can function adequately at the mental age of 3 years, at which level a well-differentiated circle can be drawn (see also figures A and 2). The rotation of the slanted portion of figure 5 may be a manifestation of angulation difficulty similar to that found in figure 3, or an attempt to avoid a collision with figure 2. If the latter is the case, it implies adequate ego functioning, suggested previously by the patient's sequence, and tends to rule out a psychotic process.

Fragmentation and simplification again occur in figure 6. Furthermore, flattening of the curves takes place and they are reproduced as a scribble. This treatment of figure 6 is characteristic of children at the five year level (see ref. 4, p. 126), and adds weight to the inference of mental deficiency. The difficulty with the curves (flattening) also suggests underreaction to emotional stimuli.

Figure 7 again manifests fragmentation and simplification. Furthermore, the patient is unable to reproduce a hexagonal shape. At this point, there is clearly indicated an inability to perform complex visual-motoric coordinations, such difficulty being probably of maturational origin.

The hexagonal shape in figure 8 is simplified to an acceptable rectangle. The internal diamond is inadequately drawn as an irregular six-sided figure. Difficulty with the diamond shape is consistent with the treatment of the oblique square in figure A. The handling of this Gestalt is typical of the mental defective (retrogression, simplification and inability to perceive and complete complex Gestalten).

The distortions apparent in this test record could be the result of one of several clinical syndromes. These entities are: schizophrenia, organic brain damage, primary mental deficiency, and mental deficiency secondary to organic brain damage.

In making a differential diagnosis, it should be noted that we would expect, both in cases of schizophrenia and of organic brain damage, evidence in the test record of variable levels of adjustment and maturity. That is to say, in both of these types of disorder, the patient would have reached relatively high levels of maturational development but then, as a result of schizophrenic regressions or organic involvement, would have lost "this maturity" and would make an adjustment at a more primitive level on some but not *all* of the Gestalten. From a theoretical point of view, such retrogression is never complete; it is irregular and evidence of the higher level of adjustment persists in behavior as well as in test data. Turning to the record, we find that the patient quite adequately reproduces the circular forms at every opportunity. Furthermore, from the adequate open square of figure 4 and the rectangular form produced in figure 8, we infer that the patient is capable of producting the square shape, which indicates functioning at the 5 year level. The diamond shape (7 year level) is failed at every opportunity, as is the hexagonal shape. This patient's "even" functioning is not consistent with either schizophrenia or organic brain damage.

The patient's relatively adequate ego functions, manifested in methodical sequence, appropriate size of the Gestalten and the treatment of figure 5 in which a possible collision is avoided, also is contraindicative of a psychosis.

Organic brain damage can also be ruled out on the additional basis of the patient's fairly good coordination, particularly the regularity of her handling of the dots (see the test protocol in Chapter X for comparison), the even quality of lines, and the over-all consistent appearance of the test record.

On the other hand, the patient's adequate functioning at a lower maturational level and total inability to function at higher levels, consistent fragmentations, and simplifications of all figures involving disparate elements are striking evidence of mental deficiency. Since we find no evidence of organic brain damage the diagnostic impression is that of primary mental deficiency.

The patient's IQ can also be estimated from this data. She is capable of maturational behavior at the five year level (drawing a square) but not at the seven year level (drawing a diamond).[41] The level of some of her other reproductions, particularly figure 5, suggests a probable mental age of six. The estimated IQ is, therefore, 37.

The patient's inadequately developed maturational level makes inferences derived from many of the test factors highly unreliable. Hypotheses associated with the factors of angulation difficulty and the like must now be evaluated more cautiously. But other factors such as sequence, use of space, size and line quality are little affected by maturational factors. On the basis of hypotheses developed from these latter factors we can conclude that the patient's ego strength is appropriate for her level of maturation, that she has a generally passive orientation, tends to suppress and internalize tension, inhibits impulses and hostility. She is likely to be compliant and cooperative, with little danger of impulsive acting-out. These personality characteristics have considerable implications for educational and/or vocational management.

The patient has always been regarded as being "slow." The mother's pregnancy was uneventful and the birth was an easy one. The medical history is essentially noncontributory and there is no evidence of injury or illness of a nature that might have contributed to her deficiency.

She lives at home and is described by her parents as a well-behaved, cooperative and docile person. She never leaves the house unless she is accompanied by a member of the family.

The patient occupies her time by watching television, doing housework, "sewing" and "reading." She can recognize letters as well as simple, one-syllable words and she spells out words to her mother who pronounces them for her.

Her clinical appearance was congruent with her parents' description. She was neatly dressed and well-groomed. In general, her orientation was passive and she did manifest awareness of her inadequacies, as her comments during the testing indicated, although she also attempted to cover them over by talking about her "reading and studying."

The patient's Wechsler-Bellevue summary follows:

Verbal		*Performance*	
Information	3	Picture arrangement	3
Comprehension	2	Picture completion	0
Digit span	0	Block design	1
Arithmetic	0	Object assembly	0
Similarities	2	Digit symbol	4

Verbal IQ   53
Performance IQ   46
Full Scale IQ   46

The patient's verbalizations were at an extremely concrete level and she approached tasks that called for reasoning (picture arrangement, block design, object assembly) in a trial and error fashion. Her IQ scores and the relatively even level of her test performance support the diagnostic impression of primary mental deficiency.

PART III

XII

Special Problems in Assessment:

Malingering, Resistance,

Physical Handicap

In this chapter we shall discuss some of the special problems which may be encountered in the administration of the RBGT and suggest some procedures for dealing with them. Special conditions always require some modification in the methods of preparing the patient or in methods of administering the test, and the experienced clinician will devise *ad hoc* methods according to the nature of the problem. Of course, such deviations from the "standard" procedures will necessitate consideration of the possible effects of the variation upon the evaluation of the responses. However, to assume that any patient may be expected to give results that may be interpreted in terms of the principles and findings presented in the preceding chapters even when there are significant factors interfering with the administration is to neglect some obvious data from "clinical life." On the other hand, variations in procedure should not be attempted without careful consideration, *in advance*, of the implications of such changes in method.

Malingering

The problem of malingering was touched on briefly in Chapter IV. The most simple and effective procedure for dealing with cases of suspected malingering on the RBGT is to make no comment on the performance and then to readminister the test, especially the *copy phase*, some time later, optimally a week later, by which time it may be assumed that the patient will have forgotton most of the special distortions which he performed originally.

141

In dealing with cases of malingering it is well to avoid special procedures for testing this factor until a considerable amount of information about the patient is acquired in the regular course of clinical investigation. After such information has been acquired, some understanding of the nature of the malingering and its relationship to the psychopathology which the patient may have, may be obtained. As is well known, malingering most frequently occurs on a conscious basis in individuals with psychopathic personality or character disorders. In such cases, it may be possible to persuade the patient to ally himself with the examiner in terms of his own best interests—to help the clinic or institution to deal with him more sympathetically as well as understandingly. If this can be done, simple readministration of the test may give more adequate results. In the case of patients with paranoid difficulties, the problems which one must deal with are quite different and, possibly, little can be accomplished to disentangle the paranoid defense from the malingering aspects of the character. Similarly, with other types of problems, whatever special procedures may be indicated will rest upon the clinician's evaluation of the nature of the problem.

A special problem is the case of the individual brought for psychological evaluation by virtue of some legal action which is pending, as in court cases or in prison situations. In such instances the reality may motivate the examinee to attempt to conceal as much as possible or to give a more pathologic picture than is really the case. The first problem, therefore, may be simply that of deciding whether or not there is malingering and whether or not there is some severe form of psychopathology. Let us assume that the RBGT, *copy phase*, is readministered to such an examinee about a week after the original administration. The examiner may then compare the results of the two tests and note whether stylistic features have been significantly modified and whether the types of distortions have been changed in the interim. If either or both of these conditions obtains, one may assume that malingering on either or both occasions occurred. The task then is to confront the examinee with the marked discrepancies, frankly tell him that you, the examiner, are aware that he has been malingering, and then proceed to require that he now do his best so that an appropriate evaluation may be made. It is not suggested that such an approach will always or usually causes the examinee to change his attitude significantly, but, at least, confirmation of the hypothesis that malingering has taken place may be obtained, and some new and more valid RBGT data may also be obtained.

When there is insufficient time for readministration at a later date, a simple technique may be employed that may be about as effective. At least, in those instances in which this approach was employed, by one of the authors in military situations, it seemed quite effective. As soon as the *copy phase* has been completed, if malingering is suspected, the examiner then says something to the effect, "Now, we'll do this an entirely different way. I'm going to change something about the way I give these cards to you and I want you to be sure to copy the *new designs* exactly as you see them on the cards." The examiner, having first removed the RBGT cards from sight along with the results of the examinee's *copy phase*, then gives the examinee a new batch of paper and presents the cards again, one at a time, this time placing each card before the examinee in the *reverse of the original position* (i.e., the top of the card is now at the bottom). Moreover, the *order of presentation is changed*, starting with figure 4 instead of A, thus: 4, 5, 6, 7, 8, then A, 1, 2, and 3. For many of the designs a reversal of position creates a modified Gestalt, especially on figures 4, 5, 7, and on 2. Thus, one may examine the way in which these figures, especially, are reproduced during the second administration, noting whether the same or different types of modifications of Gestalten occurred as on the original presentation. Significant changes in the scoring factors presented in Chapter V makes the record suspect in terms of malingering. Moreover, with the changed order of presentation of cards, the examinee may suspect that he must change his sequence and use of space. However, nonmalingerers *do not show significant changes in these factors*, according to our experience. Thus, the new presentation gives us a check on the consistency in stylistic features and on specific modifications of Gestalten—and significant changes are suspect. The examiner may then decide whether he wishes to confront the examinee with any evidence of malingering and proceed with further testing, if indicated.

Resistance

There are a great variety of problems which fall in the general category of resistance. These may include resistance on an unconscious basis and resistance on a conscious basis. It is believed that the former phenomena can best be dealt with in a therapeutic relationship and that changes in such phenomena will result, primarily, from changes in the personality of the individual. However, conscious resistance is important in that it tends to produce a record which offers a less adequate basis for diagnosis and prediction. Hence, the examiner will wish to decrease, as much as possible, such resistance phenomena before, or possibly during, the administration of the test. It is to this problem that we shall give some attention now.

One source of conscious resistance is the examinee's fear that he cannot draw well and that he will, therefore, give a less satisfactory impression than he would like. It is well, in such instances, to take ample time to discuss the nature of the test, emphasizing in a variety of ways that drawing ability, per se, has no bearing on the evaluation of the results, but that, rather, the

way in which the individual goes about doing the test is of primary significance. There may also be some discussion of the patient's fearful attitude
toward drawing. And, finally, the patient may be reassured that, in the first
phase of the test at least, the task is a relatively simple one, to copy simple
geometric designs with the cards directly in front of him. During the test,
the examiner's interest and approval of how well the patient is doing will,
of course, also be important.

Another common source of resistance derives from the patient's anxiety
concerning the manifestation of his behavior in the rather intimate person-
to-person relationship which the examination involves. As we have noted
in Chapter IV, the RBGT tends to be at the low end of the scale in terms
of close examiner-examinee interrelationships, the test acting as a kind of
screen between the two participants. However, being observed while working
at the test materials may be highly threatening for some patients. In such
instances, it is recommended that the examiner make an obvious effort to
demonstrate that he is not observing the examinee closely and that he is
not making notes. He may, for example, busy himself with some other
activity while the patient is working on each card, attending to the examinee
only at the beginning of the reproduction of each design to assure himself
that the card is being maintained in its correct position, and the like. Problems of this kind have led the authors to abandon the use of the face-to-face
situation (across a desk) for the examining situation. It is preferred to sit
alongside and slightly behind the examinee, sometimes at a fairly good distance away. Of course, some important observational data may be lost if
careful attention is not directed to the patient's behavior during the test,
but the gain in the general relationship may be far more important in some
cases.

We have suggested that the RBGT is a good buffer test because of its
innocuous nature (for most patients). Since drawing, and the copying of
designs which may have sexual implications for some patients, may, however, be quite threatening in some instances, it would be well to delay testing
with the RBGT in such circumstances until a later stage of the general
testing. Sometimes, freehand drawing may help the patient to relax or to
gain some assurance. In any case, careful attention to the overt attitudes
of the patient to this test should be given in deciding when, whether, and
how to give it.

Physical Handicap

If the patient's physical condition seriously interferes with his performance
on the RBGT it may be desirable to avoid the use of this test (and to substi-
tute some other, more appropriate procedure). Nevertheless, it may be con-

sidered desirable to administer this test despite obvious physical limitations on the part of the patient. If this is done, the first problem which should be given careful attention is an accurate summary of the nature of the patient's physical limitations and of any modifications in test procedure. The statement of variations in procedure can then become an integral part of the record for subsequent use in evaluating the significance of the results.

Some conditions have a "general" effect upon the patient's performance, the nature of which may be assessed by readministering the test when this condition has abated. For example, following administration of drugs or following electroshock therapy, if the interval between the clinical treatment and the test administration is "short," the results of successive administration(s) may be utilized to evaluate the effect of the particular treatment in terms of immediate and longer range intervals. In such cases no special adaptation in methods of administration may be considered necessary, but the specific nature of the clinical treatment and its (time) relationship to the testing should be carefully specified, of course.

When the dominant hand of the patient is temporarily disabled, due to accident, disease, or surgery, it may be possible to have the patient take the test with the other hand. In such instances, careful evaluation of the previous history of handedness preference and experience should be attempted. In addition, special aids may be necessary during the test administration. For example, the examiner may assist by holding the paper on which the responses are made or by providing some mechanical means to assist the patient in dealing with the test materials. A number of test factors would then not be available for the usual type of interpretation. The most important of these would include: line quality and direction of line movement; closure difficulty; change in size of parts of whole figures; spacing. On the other hand, such factors as destruction of Gestalt, simplification, sequence, curved versus straight line modifications would still have great significance.

Other conditions may require different adaptations in procedure with different cautions during the evaluative process. As an illustration of the wide variety of problems which may confront the clinician we may mention such conditions as delirium tremens, hysterical and nonfunctional paralyses, and severe physical debilitation due to severe and chronic anxiety, exhaustion, anemia, and the like. In such conditions, the patient's hand may be held or supported, rest periods may be required, and placement of the stimulus cards and drawing materials may have to be altered to meet the patient's needs. The specific adaptations required and the consequent effect upon the performance will then have to be given special and different evaluation in each instance.

In the case of handicaps involving severe limitations of vision or total blindness, the examiner may wish to prepare similar but different examination materials. For instance, a few workers have prepared copies of the Gestalten in which the figures are reproduced not with line drawings but with raised, worsted yarn. The patient can then feel the figures with his fingers and attempt to reproduce them in the usual manner. It is to be understood, of course, that in cases such as this, extreme care must be exercised in interpretation of the findings. The test is now so different in character that it constitutes a relatively different situation. Nevertheless, some test factors may still have similar significance to that of factors in "normal" circumstances. Sequence, methods of work, distortions of straight and curved line figures, and the like, may be especially useful for evaluative purposes, but others like spacing, collision tendencies, and crossing and closure problems may be of relatively little or no value.

It should be clear, also, that the clinician will have to be very careful to orient the patient and prepare him for the test in terms that are quite different from those he would employ in normal circumstances. Emphasis can be placed on "seeing how the patient goes about working at this problem" rather than on "copying the figures accurately." The patient may also need to be reassured that careful attention to the patient's special physical limitations will be taken into account in evaluating the performance.

Despite the need to maintain great care in preparing the patient, modifying the methods of administration, and summarizing the special procedures which are employed, it can be surprising, in many instances, how revealing the test results may be. Of course, occasionally more can be gained from evaluation of how the patient goes about tackling the unusual problem which he has rather than from the specific results he achieves with the reproduction of the figures. But often, even the reproductions themselves may lend themselves to important evaluations concerning the nature of the patient's personality problems.

XIII

The Use of the RBGT With Children:
Case Illustration

The psychological evaluation of children and young adolescents generally poses problems of communication and motivation. Initially, the clinician must contend with the motivation of his young patient. It is only rarely that the child or young adolescent has any real awareness of his own problems and consequently he is frequently brought to the psychologist by a parent or other interested adult. When the patient is less than 10 years of age, testing per se is not often regarded as threatening, and if structured as a play situation, may be entered into eagerly by the child. If the test materials resemble the usual toys of the child or are common in his daily experience, evaluation may be facilitated. In this respect drawing tests such as the "Draw a Person," "House, Tree, Person," and the like are frequently used because they take advantage of the child's educational experiences in which drawing plays so large a role. They are also geared to the satisfactions he derives in using pencil and paper for motoric expression as he gains active mastery of his environment.

The RBGT fits into this schema very neatly. Not only can it easily be structured as a drawing game but it has the added advantage of providing the child with a stimulus to copy, thus further reducing resistance and fearfulness that may be experienced by him if he is merely presented with a blank sheet of paper and literally encouraged to "produce."

Furthermore, many children under 10 years of age have relatively limited verbal facilities; their scope of vocabulary is narrow and their adjustment and communication are basically in terms of doing rather than thinking and saying. Hence, evaluation by means other than verbal will most likely produce test data of greater clinical significance.

In dealing with nonadult patients 10 years or older, the problems of

147

motivation and communication may be interrelated. The young adolescent who is not motivated to face his problems and who must be evaluated economically, from a time standpoint, is apt to be both fearful and defensive and thus inhibit communication to the point at which verbal techniques result in sparse and meagre protocols. Moreover, patients over 10 years of age are fairly sophisticated and are less likely to be ensnared by the "let's play games" gambit. As contrasted to younger children, they more usually recognize the testing procedure for what it is and react accordingly. In this kind of situation, the RBGT, particularly the *copy phase*, may serve as a useful buffer. The semistructured aspects of the test, i.e., copying designs, is not likely to produce the same degree of resistance as presenting the patient with a blank sheet of paper and asking him to draw something "off the top of his head." The nonverbal aspects of the RBGT also reduce the chances of inhibitory tendencies which limit the patient's responsivity.

Administration of the RBGT to children has been previously discussed in Chapter IV. If modifications of the basic procedure are necessary, appropriate note should be made so that these changes are considered when the record is analyzed.

When the test is utilized with adolescents who are overtly resistant, it is usually best to present the test in a matter of fact way, without implying that the examiner is at all concerned with obtaining absolute and full cooperation. At an appropriate time, the examiner should casually place a stack of paper on the desk, put one sheet and a pencil before the patient and say, "I'm going to show you some cards that have designs on them. Copy them just the way you see them." If the patient replies that he cannot draw, he may be told, "That's not important; just copy them the best you can." This technique has been found effective with resistant patients who do not go so far as to refuse completely to participate in their evaluation. Furthermore, the RBGT can provide data that go beyond the stick figure response to the DAP, "It doesn't remind me of anything" to the Rorschach, or "A couple of people talking" to cards of the TAT.

Although RBGT test factors presumably have greater significance for patients 18 years of age or older, since with such patients we have reasonable assurance that distortions in Gestalten are *not* due to maturational factors, the test nevertheless can provide valuable data for younger patients.

Test factors not greatly affected by age are: sequence, position of the first drawing, use of space, use of the margin, shift in the position of the stimulus cards and paper, and size.[4, 6, 7]

Factors inversely related to age (i.e., the younger the child, the more likely will maturation be of significance) are: rotation, closure, angulation, simplification, fragmentation and crossing.[4, 10]

The relationship of other factors to age (under 18) are not clearly specifiable at this time.

In the analysis of a child's record (as in the case of mental deficiency) consistent presence or absence of a factor suggests maturational causes; the inconsistent appearance of a test factor is more likely related to emotional factors. Analysis proceeds by estimating the maturational age of the child. Variations from this level are then interpreted by the inferential method previously discussed.

Even though the test is not recommended for use with children younger than seven years of age, estimates of maturity and ego functioning in the case of younger children is possible. Adequate reproduction of the circular form is expected in the case of the average three year old. The circles in figures A and 2 are significant indicators of the level of maturational development. The average five year old can be expected to reproduce adequately the square form in figure 4, and the diamond form in figure 8 and figure A can be reproduced by the seven year old.

Furthermore, the manner in which the young child arranges sequence, modifies size and uses space can provide valuable information regarding the differentiation of the self and organization of the ego in spite of the presence or absence of other test factors. Ability to contain impulses and use of compulsive mechanisms and other datum can also be inferred from these test protocols.

The following case will illustrate the use of the RBGT with an adolescent girl. The RBGT material was administered by a psychologist in one of the public school systems in a city in Michigan and was submitted to one of the authors for a "blind" analysis. The following information was supplied: "Female subject, age 14 years, 10 months. Referred for psychological evaluation because of dull, listless attitude. Making no academic progress." The pupil was in a special class at the time of testing. There were no physical handicaps and there was no history of any serious illness. The girl was left-handed.*

It will be noted that the drawings are crowded into the bottom two-thirds of the page, showing a generally constricted use of space, and that the spacing between successive drawings is uneven and excessive. Thus, the first inferences one can draw from this general stylistic feature is that this girl is fearful in her orientation to the world, her ego controls function in an

---

*This analysis, done on a "blind" basis, was presented at a conference of School Diagnosticians of Michigan on October 12, 1958. The test protocols were made available by R. C. Carelton.

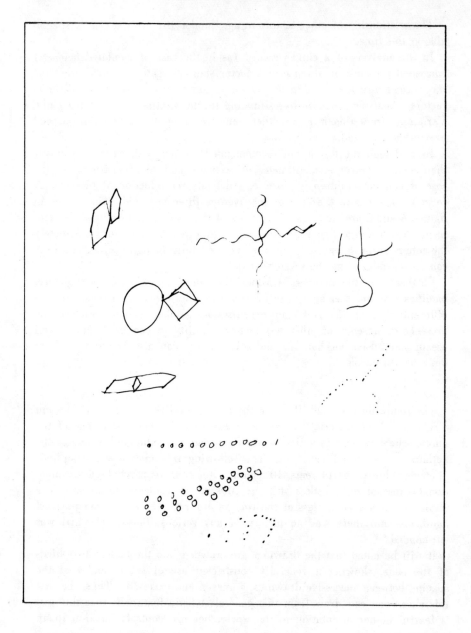

PLATE 13   An Adolescent Record (copy phase).

irregular fashion, she responds to traumatic material with withdrawal, and she shows some indications of poor anticipatory planning.

An analysis of the sequence of her drawings indicates that this is irregular and involves not only more than two changes in direction of sequence but also a general counterclockwise sequence, the total set of drawings comprising a circular emplacement of figure A by means of the other figures. The irregular sequence is indicative of considerable emotional disturbance, neurotic in proportions. The general direction of movement is indicative of latent and internalized aggression. Most likely, she is controlled in her overt behavior but is capable of considerable acting-out.

Placement of figure A slightly off-center and to the left is atypical and suggests, again, that this patient is fearful and tends toward a passive, withdrawn orientation with respect to the world. Taken together with the other evidence adduced thus far, we are led to the inference that this girl is highly fearful of authority figures. The cumulative evidence also suggests that ego controls may only be marginal and oppositional tendencies may be present.

There are no indications of collision, but there is a possible indication of a collision tendency between figures 1 and 2, for reasons which will be suggested later when these figures are analyzed. Again, the inference that ego controls are not very effective is confirmed.

One may also note that this girl does not use the margin as a prop, that her line quality is good although variable, and that the general size of her reproductions is decreased. We may infer that there is some degree of egocentrism, that overtly she does not appear to be greatly disturbed, and that her behavior is generally inhibited and withdrawn.

Whatever else may be uncovered as contributing to her poor academic work, it is clear that emotional disturbance is fairly pronounced, even though not readily observable, and contributes to her school difficulties.

An examination of the specific figures now follows. We have already noted the atypical placement of figure A and commented on it. Additionally, one may note that the circle is somewhat elliptical in shape, that the square is reproduced relatively small in size and required two attempts for completion (one attempt resulting in a markedly reduced figure), that closure difficulties, particularly in the square, are evident, and that there is poor line quality in part of the square. The elliptical and vertical distortion of the circle together with the reduction in size of the square suggests that the distortions are not purely perceptual (or due to mental retardation) but are traumatic and are a reaction to fearfulness of authority figures. Further, it is suggested that this girl's psychosexual development is essentially infantile in quality, that her primary identification is female in character, and that her identification with a male figure, during the oedipal period, was inadequate. There is a suggestion of neurotic inhibition and shyness in hetereosexual relationships.

The reproduction of figure 1 is quite interesting and offers confirmation of some of our hypotheses plus some new inferences. It will be noted that she has drawn 12 circles, instead of 12 dots, and in addition has added a dash. There is a tendency for the dots to become increasingly larger (from left to right). She has placed dots in some of the circles. The circles are placed rather closely together in a cohesive (reduced) lateral orientation. The inferences are that this girl shows infantile modes of adaptation and that (considering the simplification represented by the circles, instead of dots, plus the obsessive feature of placing dots within the circles) she manifests some indications of both oral and anal fixations. There is also the suggestion, indicated for the first time, of some mild organic deficit. There is also a tendency toward impulsive acting-out (the dash and the dots). She probably has low frustration tolerance and tends to adjust by passivity and by seeking a simplified, protected milieu in which to function.

Figure 2 contains 9 instead of 10 columns of circles. The drawing clearly indicates this girl's great difficulty with the perceptual problem of the angulated columns of circles. Her attempt on the first column is inadequate (she produces a curved column instead of an angulated column). Then she makes a compensatory attempt to deal with the problem of angulation, producing a rotation of the whole figure in a counterclockwise orientation. The impression is gathered that there has been some mild (at least) and diffuse intracranial damage. The postulated anal and obsessive controls break down in the face of this figure without clear ground-figure separation. Some tendency toward narcissism and depression are evident. This type of production, in the light of all of the preceding evidence, raises the question of some such condition as encephalitis despite the fact that the history has indicated no serious illnesses.

Figure 3 is reduced in the vertical plane; it contains an excessive number of dots in the right, peripheral segment; there is a rotation in a counterclockwise direction; and there is a reduced angulation in the segment of the arrowhead toward the left portion of the figure. The inferences of passivity and oppositional features of the personality, previously inferred, are reinforced. Denial and isolation are suggested as possible defense mechanisms. This girl's loss of perspective and her inability to attend to details despite an obvious effort to try to do so suggests either lack of mental capacity or some organic deficit, more likely the latter. Poor interpersonal relations and mild depressive trends are suggested.

Figure 4 is placed in a position above figure A. The curved portion shows fine motor incoordination and, in general, is much larger than the open square. There is a compensatory loop at the left end of the curve. Closure difficulty is pronounced. The open square appears to have been done quickly or impulsively, as if to get it over with quickly. The most striking inferences are: inability to discharge effect appropriately, fearfulness in interpersonal relations, and inability to tolerate emotional traumata.

Figure 5 shows another change in sequence. The number of dots in both portions of the figure is excessive. There is a slight clockwise rotation of the entire figure. The line quality of the dots is highly uneven; there are good dots, some dashes, and some blurred dots. The semicircle is flattened somewhat. Despite the obvious difficulties which this figure presents, the general Gestalt is preserved, indicating that mental retardation as a primary factor is not likely to be the major factor in this case, and suggesting careful examination of the more difficult figures to check on this hypothesis. There is considerable evidence of some kind of compensatory control operating as a means of maintaining or attempting to maintain her adjustment. This girl appears to be quite inhibited, but her performance is definitely uneven.

Figure 6 manifests another change of sequence. The curves are made to intersect at right angles. The waves in the curves are uneven and compensatory loops are added. The balanced quality of this production is further evidence of this girl's attempt to conform. She is fearful of emotional situations (stimuli), and shows poor affective discharge. There is occasional impulsivity despite strong needs to control and inhibit. The crossing difficulty which the figures show is indicative of poor interpersonal relations.

Figure 7 shows the classic characteristic of organic difficulty. This girl has difficulty with the problem of overlapping figures and "solves" it by separating the figures and thus reproducing each part accurately. Thus the general Gestalt is lost, but there is an excellent reproduction of the difficult, hexagonal figures and they are placed tangentially to each other. In addition to the simplification which is evident, closure difficulty is present. The figures are reduced in size. Impressions: mild cortical damage for which there is some compensation—hence, it is of considerable duration; denial and withdrawal are prominent methods of defense; fearfulness of being rejected by authority figures; limited capacity for fantasy.

The Gestalt of figure 8 is maintained, although there is considerable difficulty with the left, lower obtuse angle. That this is not due simply to the production of obtuse angles is evident in terms of success with this problem on figures A and 7. The counterclockwise rotation of the figure (slight), the closure difficulty, and the marked reduction in size of the reproduction, taken together, suggest that this girl's problems in interpersonal relationships are pronounced, that her organic problem is a contributory factor in her adjustment, that inhibition may be a central problem in the personality (with occasional acting-out to discharge pent-up drives), that she tends to be

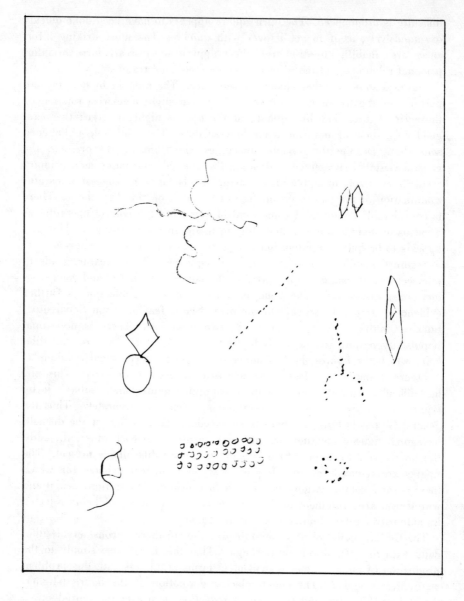

PLATE 14   An Adolescent Record (elaboration phase).

apathetic and depressed. The general hypothesis of considerable, compensatory overcontrol appears to be well founded.

Now we can turn our attention to the elaborations produced by this patient. (See Plate 14.)

It will be noted that all nine figures were administered. The general stylistic features concerning spacing and sequence that were noted for the *copy phase* of the test are maintained or exaggerated in the *elaboration phase*. Line quality appears to be slightly improved. Moreover, all of the Gestalten are clearly recognizable in the elaborations, i.e., this patient was not free enough to depart greatly from the stimulus figures.

Figure A is reproduced accurately (more so than in the *copy phase*), but the design is rotated in a counterclockwise direction so that the square is placed on top of the circle. As in the *copy phase*, there is considerable difficulty with the square, and closure difficulty appears prominently on this part of the figure. Thus, we can strengthen our confidence in the hypotheses we advanced originally for this figure in the first phase of the test.

Figure 1 is composed, now, entirely of dashes instead of dots, the whole figure being placed in a counterclockwise orientation. The impulsive features of the personality, restrained by the strong compensatory defenses, are evident, as is also the attempt to compensate for the pronounced depressive trends of this patient.

On figure 2, the loss of angulation is now frankly admitted. The figure is reproduced as a rectangle (approximately), cohesion is evident, the extra dots are again evident (sometimes placed outside of the circles), and closure difficulty is also noted. Once again, there is a rather neat set of confirmations of the hypotheses advanced originally for figure 2.

Figure 3 shows cohesion, but the essential features of the Gestalt are maintained. There is a slight tendency toward perseveration (type A) in that some of the dots are replaced by circles. The output on this figure is obviously uneven. The organic features of this record and the strong needs to guard against impulsive acting-out are confirmed.

On figure 4, the patient attempts to deal with the threat which the curved portion of the figure in the original stimulus presents. She does this by placing the open square inside the lower portion of the curve in such a way as to close the square (making it into a triangle more than a square), and reducing the apparent curvilinearity of the other portion of the Gestalt. The entire figure is reduced in size. The compensatory loop is still present. Again, our original hypotheses for this figure tend to be confirmed.

Figure 5 again shows the counterclockwise rotation noted in the *copy phase*; the secant is elongated (overcompensatory size) and is drawn at approximately a right-angle intersection to the base of the semicircle. The impulsivity which may characterize this girl at times is indicated by the rapidly done dots which are uneven and show relatively little effort expended in their execution. Fearfulness of authority figures is again suggested by the distortion on this figure.

It will be noted that the curvature on the elaboration of figure 6 is very poor and that these curves show very poor line quality. Again, one is struck by the right-angle intersection of the curves (a repeat of the performance on the *copy phase*). Extra or overcompensatory loops are present. It is clear that this girl is unable to respond easily to situations having strong emotional impact, but that she tries to conform. It may be inferred, further, that she uses withdrawal and isolation as defensive maneuvers.

On figure 7 the patient produces (again) two separate hexagons, drawn well but reduced in size. The size reductions tend toward micropsia. Both figures are presented in a vertical orientation. There is an extra line inserted in the right portion of the figure. Closure difficulty is also present. Hypotheses similar to those made in connection with the copy phase may again be offered. There is further evidence that cortical damage, if present, is mild and that relatively good compensation has been effected. Difficulty in interpersonal relationships and the use of defenses involving denial and withdrawal are again suggested.

It is most interesting that figure 8 is presented in a vertical orientation, suggesting the strong compensatory attempts in dealing with authority symbols or, possibly, some perseveratory effect (organic) due to the vertical orientation of figure 7 and the "freedom" to modify the figure, as the directions suggested. The small, separated, internal diamond suggests the feelings of inadequacy concerning her identity and her feelings of impotence. The accurate production of both acute and obtuse angles tends to reinforce the previous suggestions that mental retardation as the primary problem is not sufficient to account for her difficulties.

Turning now to her associations (all of them given to the original stimulus figures), we find the following. Her association to figure A is, "Looks like a triangle with a circle in the middle." The misinterpretation of the stimulus may be due either to retardation or organic problems or both, but the language level and rhetoric suggest organicity as a more likely factor. The literal quality of the association is consistent with such defenses as isolation and denial. These data suggest that this girl tends to be withdrawn, narcissistic and self-protective.

Figure 1 is associated with, "That looks like a line of dots." Again the self-protective and literal qualities of this response are evident. She is fearful of telling the examiner too much about herself (or is unable to). The next association, to figure 2, "That looks like little . . . a cookies, sorta like cookies," give us some indication of the oral, dependent needs of this individual, and suggests a possible strategy (that of supplying rather than frustrating her oral needs) in psychotherapy or other forms of interpersonal help.

Figure 3 is again given a literal association: "That looks like a triangle." The association of "triangle" suggests the use of the literal aspect of part of the stimulus for the whole, and indicates the possibility that she has been traumatized by the male, phallic symbol. Her literalness in associating may, therefore, be interpreted as her defensive means of isolating the traumatic impact of this kind of stimulus.

The association of, "That looks like the design of a duck or something," given to figure 4, suggests her passive orientation, possibly her strong oral needs, and suggests connotations of a dependent nature. The possible regressive feature (of a duck in water, which may be implied), and the possible "quacking" noise of the duck as a warning signal or as a call for help should not be overlooked. The associations are now getting richer in quality, and the next one, given to figure 5, is quite revealing: "That looks like a . . . looks like a kettle upside down." The position of the kettle (upside down) suggests her own disturbed feeling state, and the total association has dependent, oral, passive, and oppositional qualities.

Figure 6 is associated to with, "That looks like a plain design." Here, again, is retreat into literalness, emphasized by the reiteration that this figure not only is a design (therefore means little) but is a "plain design" (therefore surely not meaningful). This girl's difficulties with figure 6 were noted on both the *copy phase* and the *elaboration phase*, and it was suggested that she was unable to deal adequately with situations having strong affective connotations. Her failure to give anything other than her present response is confirmatory of the traumatic impact this figure has upon her.

Figure 7 is seen as, "That looks like a . . . a rocket, umh . . . umh. . . ." Although rockets are fairly frequently seen by the clinical population as associations to this figure (and figure 8), such responses are closely correlated with indications of anxiety, especially of the latent variety. There is the suggestion of pent-up internal tension and of readiness for explosion (or acting-out).

Figure 8 is seen as, "That looks like a pencil with a triangle in the middle." This response suggests her fear of being hurt (her castration anxiety), or her fear as a result of having been hurt. The association of "pencil" is an effective one for translating a phallic symbol into a conventional, socially appropriate one. There are many other possible implications of her association, such as the literal suggestion of the "triangle" (a repetitive association) in terms of the oedipal triangle (a hunch that is given only in the light of so much other evidence in the record as part of her etiologic history), and her sense of inadequacy (based on the association of "triangle in the middle" and her performance on this part of the figure in the elaboration of the figure which she produced).

On the basis of the above analysis, the following summary interpretation is offered. This is the record of a 15 year old girl who is markedly inhibited and fearful in her behavior. There is considerable evidence of some mild, diffuse organic damage, probably occurring in early childhood (say, between five and seven years of age), and possibly being an encephalitic condition. She appears to have developed relatively fair compensation for the intracranial damage over the years but the organic factor is still a handicap in her adjustment. However, her central problem appears to be that of inhibition on a neurotic basis, accompanied by mild depression and apathy. The organic factor contributes to her present difficulty but is insufficient to explain it.

The estimate of her intellectual maturity, based on her RBGT performance, is approximately 11 years, and her intelligence quotient, based on this figure and her present chronologic age, would turn out to be 73. This rough estimate will probably serve to characterize her present school performance. Despite her attempt to cooperate on the test, there is evidence of marked impairment in intellectual functioning on the basis of neurotic inhibition. It is estimated that, if her difficulties were resolved and her severe inhibitions removed, she could function at or close to the level of average ability.

Her major methods of defending herself are withdrawal, denial and isolation. She is very fearful of rejection, in general, and is especially fearful of authority figures. She usually tries to conform, but shows fairly pronounced passive, oppositional trends. There is some regression to narcissism and oral dependent behavior. Despite this evidence of regression, she has shown some progression and has both anal and oedipal modes of adjustment. She needs, almost desperately, closeness with people, but is fearful of and not skillful at interpersonal relationships. Rather, she maintains herself at a level of superficial, quasipleasant, distant relationships. She is depressed moderately, partly because of a "lack of supplies" (for her narcissistic needs), and partly because of guilt over her impulses which she usually inhibits. There is considerable evidence that she is especially fearful of heterosexual relationships and suffers from an unresolved oedipal (electra) complex. Although her major identification is female, her self-percept is that of an inadequate person.

She has few modes for appropriate discharge of internal drives and is, in a literal sense, "bottled up." Ordinarily, she manages to conform, but because of her sensitivity to affective stimuli (with inability to respond appropriately) as well as her cumulative, internal tensions, she may be expected to act out impulsively on occasion. When such behavior emerges or when she becomes aware of her impulses toward such behavior, she is likely to become more depressed. She wants to be taken care of, and in a way her passive, pathetic and oppositional qualities require that her environment supply her with some attention and gratification. Characteristically, she remains withdrawn, aloof, and "retarded." There are flashes of good ability which she displays from time to time which may lead some observers to expect that she will soon be able to perform at a much higher level of intellectual ability, but her chronic inhibition and her depressive trends are too well encapsulated to permit such a development without intensive psychotherapy. The impression, then, is that we are not dealing with a relatively simple case of constitutional retardation but, rather, one of severe inhibition of function, especially cognitive, in a neurotic character problem in an overcontrolled, adolescent girl.

It is interesting to note, in commenting on the above "blind" summary derived from the RBGT, that many of the specific evaluations were borne out by data secured after this material had been presented. For instance, it was learned that careful medical and neurologic examination, administered when she was about six years of age, led to the diagnostic conclusion that she was then suffering from a mild case of encephalitis from which, later, she had "good recovery." Examination by the psychologist who had administered the WISC resulted in a verbal scale IQ of 75, but she did indeed also show flashes of far more superior intellectual ability than her IQ indicated. It was reported by her teachers that she was generally apathetic but occasionally displayed aggressive and antisocial behavior. She hardly ever mingled with or related to boys and was distant in her relations with girls. She seemed to respond well to lavish encouragement or to indications that she was liked and accepted.

This case illustrates how an apparent mental retardation may be caused by and conceal other underlying conditions. A formal intelligence test may give an accurate measure of present intellectual functioning but may, in cases like this, be unable to reveal the greater potential which is present or the significant factors leading to the retardation in functioning.

Bibliography

1. Aaronson, B. S., "The Porteus Maze Test and the Bender Gestalt Recall," *J. clin. Psychol.*, 1957, *13*, 186-187.
2. Basowitz, H., and Korchin, S., "Age differences in the perception of closure," *J. abnorm. soc. Psychol.*, 1957, *54*, 93-97.
3. Bell, J. E., "The case of Gregor: Interpretation of test data," *J. proj. Tech.*, 1949, *13*, 433-468.
4. Bender, L., *A Visual Motor Gestalt Test and its Clinical Use.* N. Y.: Amer. Orthopsychiat. Assoc. R. Monogr., 1938, No. 3.
5. Billingslea, F. Y., "The Bender-Gestalt: An objective scoring method and validating data," *J. clin. Psychol.*, 1948, *4*, 1-27.
6. Byrd, E., "The clinical validity of the Bender-Gestalt Test with children: A developmental comparison of children in need of psychotherapy and children judged well adjusted," *J. proj. Tech.*, 1956, *20*, 127-136.
7. Clawson, A., "The Bender Visual Motor Gestalt Test as an index of emotional disturbance in children," *J. proj. Tech.*, 1959, *23*, 198-206.
8. Cronbach, L. J., *Essentials of Psychological Testing.* N. Y.: Harper, 1960.
9. Curnutt, R. H., "The use of the Bender Gestalt with an alcoholic and non-alcoholic population," *J. clin. Psychol.*, 1953, *9*, 287-290.
10. Fabian, A. A., "Vertical rotation in visual-motor performance: Its relationship to reading reversals," *J. educ. Psychol.*, 1945, *36*, 129-154.
11. Gobetz, W., "A quantification, standardization, and validation of the Bender-Gestalt Test on normal and neurotic adults," *Psychol. Monogr.*, 1953, *67*, No. 6 (whole No. 356).
12. Goldberg, L. R., "The effectiveness of clinician's judgments: The diagnosis of organic brain damage from the Bender-Gestalt Test," *J. consult. Psychol.*, 1959, *23*, 25-33.
13. Goodenough, F. L., and Harris, D. B., "Studies in the psychology of children's drawings: II, 1928-1949," *Psychol. Bull.*, 1950, *47*, 369-433.
14. Greenbaum, R. S., "A note on the use of the word association test as an aid to interpreting the Bender-Gestalt," *J. proj. Tech.*, 1955, *19* 27-29.
15. Grinker, R. R., and Spiegel, J. P., *Men Under Stress.* Philadelphia: Blakiston, 1945.
16. Guertin, W. H., "A factor analysis of curvilinear distortions on the Bender-Gestalt," *J. clin. Psychol.*, 1954, *10*, 12-17.
17. Hammer, E. F., "An experimental study of symbolism on the Bender-Gestalt," *J. proj. Tech.*, 1954, *18*, 335-345.
18. Harriman, M., and Harriman, P. L., "The Bender Motor Gestalt Test as a measure of school readiness," *J. clin. Psychol.*, 1950, *6*, 175-177.
19. Hanvik, L. J., and Anderson, A. L., "The effect of focal brain lesions on recall and on the production of rotations in the Bender-Gestalt Test," *J. consult. Psychol.*, 1950, *14*, 197-198.

20. Hanvik, L. J., "A note on rotatoins in the Bender-Gestalt Test as predictors of EEG abnormalities in children." *J. clin. Psychol.*, 1953, *9*, 399.
21. Hoch, P., and Rachlin, H. L., "An evaluation of manic-depressive psychosis in the light of follow-up studies," *Amer. j. Psychiat.*, 1941, *97*, 831-843.
22. Hutt, M. L., "A tentative guide for the administration and interpretation of the Bender-Gestalt Test," mimeographed and distributed privately, 1945.
23. Hutt, M. L., "The Bender-Gestalt Test," in "The Case of Gregor," *J. proj. Tech.*, 1949, *13*, 443-446.
24. Hutt, M. L., "Revised Bender Visual-Motor Gestalt Test," in Weider, A. (Ed.), *Contributions toward medical psychology.* N. Y.: Ronald Press, 1950.
25. Hutt, M. L., "Interpretation of a Bender-Gestalt Record," in Shneidman, E. S. (Ed.), *Thematic Test Analyses.* N. Y.: Grune and Stratton, 1951.
26. Hutt, M. L., and Gibby, R. G., *Patterns of Abnormal Behavior.* Boston: Allyn and Bacon, 1957.
27, Hutt, M. L., "The Revised Bender Gestalt test," in Carr, A. C. (Ed.), *The Prediction of Overt Behavior Through the Use of Projective Techniques.* Springfield, Ill.: in press.
28. Mira, E., "Myokinetic psychodiagnosis: A new technique of exploring the conative trends of personality," *Proc. Roy. Soc. Med.*, 1939-40, November, April.
29. Mira, E., *Psychiatry in War.* N. Y.: Norton, 1943.
30. Niebuhr, H., Jr., and Cohen, O., "The effects of psychopathology on visual discrimination," *J. abnorm. soc. Psychol.*, 1956, *53*, 173-177.
31. Oberndorf, C. P., "Diagnostic and etiological concepts in the neuroses," Hoch, P. H., and Zubin, J. (eds.), *Current Problems in Psychiatric Diagnosis.* N. Y.: Grune and Stratton, 1953.
32. Olin, T. D., and Reznikoff, M., "A comparison of copied and recalled reproductions of the Bender-Gestalt designs," *J. proj. Tech.*, 1958, *22*, 320-327.
33. Pascal, G. R., and Suttell, B. J., *The Bender-Gestalt Test.* N. Y.: Grune and Stratton, 1951.
34. Reznikoff, M., and Olin, T. D., "Recall of the Bender-Gestalt designs by organic and schizophrenic patients: A comparative study," *J. clin. Psychol.*, 1957, *13*, 183-185.
35. Sakoda, J. M., Cohen, B. H., and Beall, G., "Test of significance for a series of statistical tests," *Psychol. Bull.*, 1954, *51*, 172-175.
36. Stewart, H., and Cunningham, S., "A note on scoring recalled figures of the Bender-Gestalt, using psychotics, non-psychotics and controls," *J. clin. Psychol.*, 1958, *14*, 257-258.
37. Story, R. I., "The Revised Bender-Gestalt and male alcoholics," *J. proj. Tech.*, 24, 186-193. 1960.
38. Suczek, R. F., and Klopfer, W. G., "Interpretation of the Bender-Gestalt Test: The associative value of the figures," *Amer. j. Orthopsychiat.*, 1952, *22*, 62-75.
39. Sullivan, J. J., and Welsh, G. S., "Results from the Bender Visual Motor Gestalt Test," in Philips, E. L., et al. (eds.), "Intelligence and Personality in Poliomyelitis." *Monogr. Soc. Res. Child Develpm.*, 1947, *12*, No. 2.
40. Tamkin, A. S., "The effectiveness of the Bender-Gestalt in differential diagnosis," *J. consult. Psychol.*, 1957, *21*, 355-357.
41. Terman, L. M., and Merrill, M. A., *Measuring Intelligence.* Boston: Houghton Mifflin, 1937.
42. Tolor, A., "A comparison of the Bender-Gestalt Test and the digit span test a measure of recall," *J. consult. Psychol.*, 1956, *20*, 305-309.

43. Tolor, A., "A comparison of several measures of psychosexual disturbances," *J. proi. Tech.*, 1957, *21*, 313-317.
44. Tolor, A., "Structural properties of the Bender-Gestalt Test association," *J. clin. Psychol.*, 1957, *13*, 176-178. (See also *J. consult. Psychol.*, 1956, *20*, 305-309.)
45. Tolor, A., "Further studies of the Bender-Gestalt Test and the digit-span test on measuring recall," *J. consult. Psychol.*, 1958, *14*, 14-18.
46. Wertheimer, M., "Studies in the theory of Gestalt psychology," *Psychol. Forch.*, 1923, *4*, 301-350.
47. Williams, H. L., Lubin, A., Gieseking, C., and Rubinstein, I., "The relation of brain injury and visual perception to block design rotation," *J. consult. Psychol.*, 1956, *20*, 275-280.
48. Zolik, E. S., "A comparison of the Bender-Gestalt reproduction of delinquents and non-delinquents," *J. clin. Psychol.*, 1958, *14*, 24-26.

Index